DEVELOP
SCIENCE
LANGUAGE

for

Physical Processes

with

10–11

year olds

Charlotte Clarke

Published by Scholastic Ltd,
Villiers House,
Clarendon Avenue,
Leamington Spa,
Warwickshire CV32 5PR
Visit our website at www.scholastic.co.uk

Printed by Alden Group Ltd, Oxford

1 2 3 4 5 6 7 8 9 0   1 2 3 4 5 6 7 8 9 0

AUTHOR
Charlotte Clarke

LITERACY CONSULTANT
Gill Matthews

EDITOR
Joel Lane

ASSISTANT EDITOR
David Sandford

SERIES DESIGNER
Rachael Hammond

COVER PHOTOGRAPHY
Martyn Chillmaid

ILLUSTRATIONS
Colin Brown

British Library Cataloguing-in-Publication Data
A catalogue record for this book is available from the British Library.

ISBN 0-439-01875-7

Designed using Adobe Pagemaker

CONTENTS

5 Introduction
6 Word list

7 Changing circuits ......*(report)*

8 Changing circuits questions ......*(higher level)*
9 Changing circuits questions ......*(lower level)*
10 Changing the number of bulbs ......*(writing instructions)*
11 True, false or opinion? ......*(evaluating statements)*
12 Adding wire ......*(generating questions)*
13 Solving problems ......*(explaining)*
14 Changing circuits concept map ......*(making a concept map)*

15 Gravity and air resistance ......*(report)*

16 Gravity and air resistance questions ......*(higher level)*
17 Gravity and air resistance questions ......*(lower level)*
18 Spot the mistakes ......*(labelling and analysing a table and graph)*
19 Measuring air resistance ......*(sequencing)*
20 Gravity and air resistance crossword ......*(reverse crossword)*

21 Measuring forces ......*(factual)*

22 Measuring forces questions ......*(higher level)*
23 Measuring forces questions ......*(lower level)*
24 Making force meters (1) ......*(analysing a graph)*
25 Making force meters (2) ......*(writing instructions)*
26 Making force meters (3) ......*(comparing and evaluating)*
27 Measuring the strength of magnets ......*(labelling)*
28 Measuring forces card game ......*(round-the-class game)*

29 Forces in action ......*(factual)*

30 Forces in action questions ......*(higher level)*
31 Forces in action questions ......*(lower level)*
32 Floating and sinking poems ......*(writing mnemonic poems)*
33 Forces in action picture words ......*(creating picture words)*
34 Forces in action summary ......*(text marking)*
35 Forces and scientists 1 ......*(information text)*
36 Forces and scientists 2 ......*(extracting information from a text)*

37 Changing pitch ......*(report)*

38 Changing pitch questions ......*(higher level)*
39 Changing pitch questions ......*(lower level)*
40 Oboestraws ......*(writing instructions)*
41 Rubber band jazz ......*(sequencing)*
42 Pitch relationships ......*(writing relationship statements)*
43 The band begins to play ......*(extracting information from a text)*
44 Changing pitch crossword ......*(reverse crossword)*

45 Loud and quiet ......*(factual)*

46 Loud and quiet questions ......*(higher level)*
47 Loud and quiet questions ......*(lower level)*
48 Making and testing earmuffs ......*(labelling)*
49 Sensing sound ......*(analysing a graph)*
50 Sound concept map ......*(making a concept map)*

CONTENTS

51 Shadows ......(factual)

52 Shadows questions ......(higher level)
53 Shadows questions ......(lower level)
54 Shadows drawing game ......(oral description)
55 Changing shadows (1) ......(sequencing)
56 Changing shadows (2) ......(analysing a graph)
57 Match the mistakes ......(matching descriptions to graphs)
58 Shadow puppets ......(summarising)

59 Reflection and seeing ......(report)

60 Reflection and seeing questions ......(higher level)
61 Reflection and seeing questions ......(lower level)
62 How we see ......(explaining)
63 Up periscope! ......(writing instructions, explaining)
64 Seeing things? ......(explaining)
65 Reflection and seeing bingo (1) ......(bingo vocabulary game)
66 Reflection and seeing bingo (2) ......(bingo vocabulary game)

67 Our Solar System ......(factual)

68 Our Solar System questions ......(higher level)
69 Our Solar System questions ......(lower level)
70 Planets database ......(completing a table)
71 Finding out about the planets ......(extracting information from a chart)
72 Making a booklet ......(book making)
73 Planet travel guide ......(using secondary sources)
74 Remembering the planets ......(writing a mnemonic)

75 Time and space ......(factual)

76 Time and space questions ......(higher level)
77 Time and space questions ......(lower level)
78 The phases of the Moon (1) ......(book making)
79 The phases of the Moon (2) ......(labelling, describing, explaining)
80 Space and time dictionary ......(making a dictionary)

81 Energy sources ......(factual)

82 Energy sources questions ......(higher level)
83 Energy sources questions ......(lower level)
84 Heating our homes ......(analysing a graph, generating questions)
85 Energy sources table ......(devising and completing a table)
86 Solar-powered oven ......(instruction writing)
87 Making vehicles ......(ordering and writing instructions)
88 Energy sources card game ......(round the class game)

89 Energy transfer ......(diary)

90 Energy transfer questions ......(higher level)
91 Energy transfer questions ......(lower level)
92 More than one type of energy? ......(describing, labelling)
93 Wasted energy ......(describing, labelling)
94 Stored energy ......(explaining)
95 Energy snap (1) ......(vocabulary and explanation game)
96 Energy snap (2) ......(vocabulary and explanation game)

INTRODUCTION

Children often struggle to remember science words. Sometimes the words seem strange or unusual, and sometimes the words we use in science have other meanings. Think about these science words: *force, material, property, sink.* If you ask a child what these words mean, you are likely to get responses such as: 'If you force someone to do something, it's not very nice'; 'My coat is made of material'; 'My things are my property'; 'The sink is where we wash up after painting'. But when children go into science lessons, we sometimes assume that they already understand a 'force' to be a push or a pull, a 'material' to be any substance, a 'property' to be how a material behaves, and 'sink' to be what some things do in water.

Science language

This series aims to give children practice in using science words, both through science activities and in 'real life' contexts, so that they become familiar with the scientific meanings of these words. Use of correct scientific vocabulary is essential for high attainment in SATs. The QCA *Scheme of Work for Science* (DfEE) for Key Stages 1 and 2 in England suggests examples of vocabulary for each of its units; although these books are not divided into exactly the same topics, the QCA vocabulary and its progressive introduction are used as the basis for the word selection here.

The science covered is divided into units based on topics from the national curricula for England, Northern Ireland, Wales and Scotland. In this book, the science is drawn from the 'Physical processes' statements for ages 10–11 relating to electricity, forces, light, sound, the Earth and space, and energy. The series of boxed letters at the bottom of each page shows in which curriculum documents the focus of each activity occurs. For example, for the text on page 88, the boxes E NI W S indicate that the activity focuses on a topic from the National Curriculum for Northern Ireland and the Scottish Guidelines.

Science literacy

The National Literacy Strategy for England suggests teaching objectives and gives examples of the types of activities that children should encounter during each year of primary school. This book uses many of these techniques for developing children's understanding and use of scientific language. The activities are mainly intended for use in science time, as they have been written with science learning objectives in mind. However, some of the activities could be used in literacy time. Science texts have already been published for use in literacy time, but many of them use science content appropriate for older children.

During literacy time you need to be focusing on language skills, not teaching new science. It is with this in mind that these sheets, drawing from age-appropriate science work, have been produced. It is also suggested that these sheets are used in literacy time only after the science content has been introduced in science time.

The series focuses on paper-based activities to develop scientific language, but it is hoped that teachers might use some of the ideas in planning practical science activities.

About this book

Each unit in this book begins with a non-fiction text that introduces some key scientific vocabulary. The key words are highlighted by bold type. The texts cover a range of non-fiction genres.

Following this text are two comprehension activities that help children to identify and understand the key words (and a range of additional science words). They are pitched at two levels:

for older or more able children

for younger or less able children.

Although the comprehension activities are designed to be used mainly during science time, you may wish to use the texts as examples of non-fiction texts in the literacy hour. The comprehension pages contain two or three types of question (a change of icon indicates a change in the type of question):

The answer can be found in the text.

Children will need to think about the answer. These questions usually elicit science understanding beyond what the text provides.

An activity aimed at developing children's literacy skills. These are optional extension activities for individual or group work, with teacher support if necessary.

Following the comprehension pages in each unit are activities to develop children's understanding and use of the key vocabulary. They include: completing charts, describing, matching graphs to descriptions, labelling, sequencing, analysing graphs and tables, making books and dictionaries, writing relationship statements, writing mnemonic poems, generating questions, text marking, writing instructions, 'round the class' card games and concept maps.

WORD LIST

Electricity words

battery
break
brightness
bulb
cell
circuit
circuit diagram
circuit symbol
complete circuit
component
electrical conductor
electrical insulator
motor
overload
short circuit
terminal
voltage

Forces words

air resistance
compress
descend
direction
distance
downwards
fall
float
force
force meter
gravity
harder
heavy
light
newton
newton meter
parachute
pull
push
opposite
sink
speed
spring
spring balance
streamlining
stretch
upthrust
weight

Sound words

earmuffs
ears
high
higher
loud
loudness
low
lower
muffle
noise
pitch
quiet
quieter
silence
silent
sound maker
soundproof
strings
tension
tuning
vibrate
vibration
volume

Light words

absence of light
angle
block
bounce
dark
darkness
eye
fuzzy
light
light ray
light source
mirror
object
opaque
outline
position
reflect
reflection
screen
see
shadow
sharp
straight lines
translucent
transparent
travels

Space words

atmosphere
axis
day
Earth
gas
heat source
Jupiter
light source
lunar month
Mars
Mercury
month
Moon
Neptune
night
orbit
phases of the Moon
planet
Pluto
rotate
rotation
satellite
Saturn
star
solar system
Sun
temperature
Uranus
Venus
waning
waxing
year

Energy words

battery
coal
device
diesel
electrical energy
energy
energy changer
energy source
energy transfer
food
fuel
gas
generate
light energy
mains
movement energy
oil
petrol
power station
release
solar cell
sound energy
stored energy
supply
thermal energy
transfer
transform
transformation

Changing circuits

These pupils were investigating different ways to change the **brightness** of **bulbs** or the **speed** of **motors** in a **circuit**. Each group made a change to one **component** in their circuit and observed the effect. They drew **circuit diagrams** of their experiments, using standard circuit **symbols** where possible.

1. Nigel and Sam

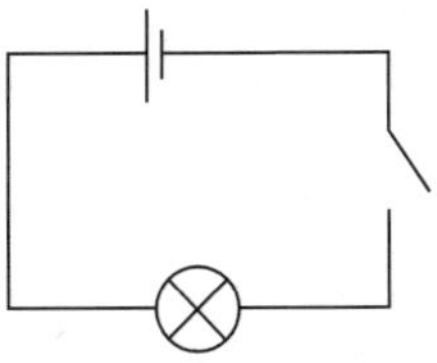

We altered the **voltage** of the **cell** in our circuit. A cell is what we usually call a **battery**. The higher the voltage of the cell, the brighter the bulb became. Eventually the bulb **blew** because we had **overloaded** the circuit.

2. Tariq and Sajid

We started off with one battery and added another each time. The more batteries we had, the faster the motor turned.

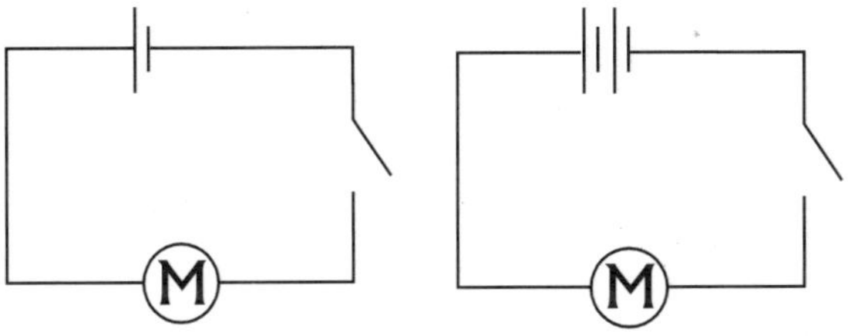

3. Jane and Celia

We tried different **electrical conductors** and **insulators** in our circuit. When we used **insulators** the bulb did not work at all. When we tried different **conductors**, some of them seemed to make the bulb light up more brightly than others, but we couldn't be sure.

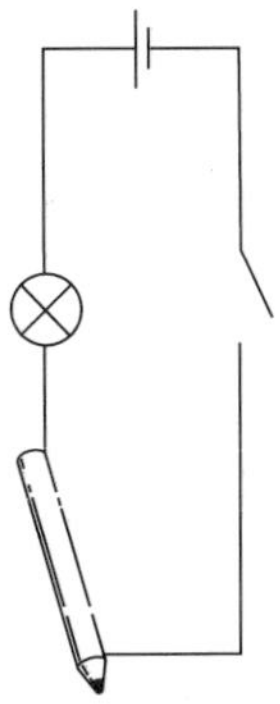

Our circuit didn't work once when we were using a conductor, but we realised that two wires were touching. This made a **short circuit**: the electricity had an easy way to get from one **terminal** of the battery to the other without passing through the bulb.

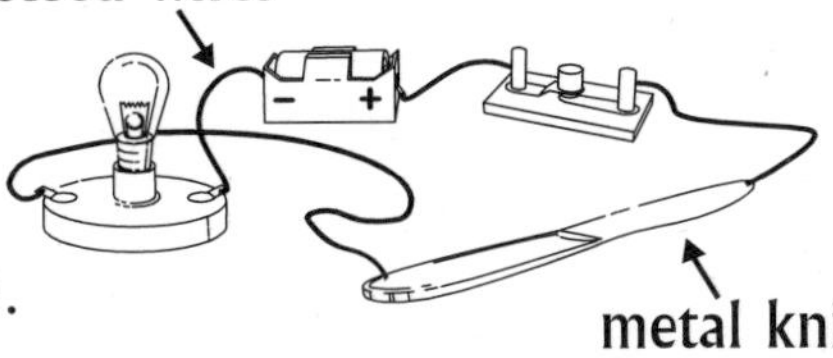

4. Colin, Liz and Peter

We made a circuit containing a long piece of wire made from a metal called nichrome. We changed the length of the wire. We found that the shorter the wire, the brighter the bulb. It was harder for the electricity to push through a longer wire.

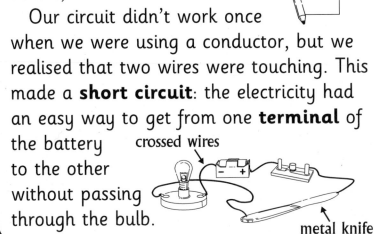

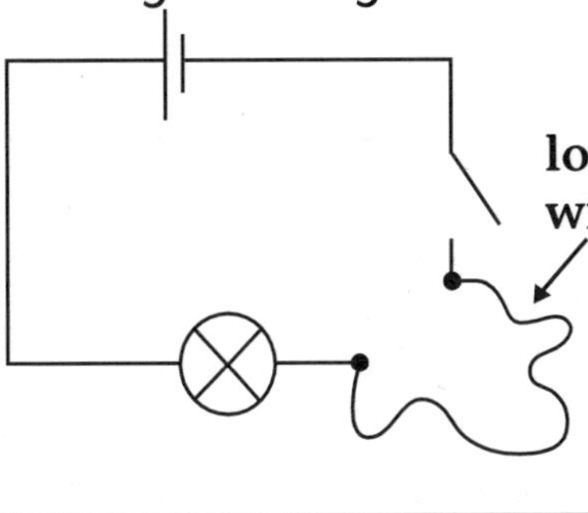

Changing circuits

1. Write down the component that each group altered.

Group	Component
1 ____	____
2 ____	____
3 ____	____
4 ____	____

2. Write a sentence to describe the relationship between the component each group altered and what they observed. One has been done for you.

Group 1: The higher the voltage of the battery, the brighter the bulb.

____

____

____

3. The groups needed to make a complete circuit with no breaks. Why?

____

4. One group had to stop their experiment. Which group was this?

Why did they stop?______________________________

____

5. Why did all the pupils draw circuit diagrams using symbols instead of drawing pictures of what they did?

____

6. What is a short circuit?______________________________

____

Write a set of instructions on another sheet to explain to Nigel and Sam how to carry out Colin, Liz and Peter's experiment.

Changing circuits

1. Each group of pupils changed one component in their circuit. What did each group change?

Nigel and Sam ______________ Tariq and Sajid ______________

Jane and Celia ______________ Colin, Liz and Peter ______________

2. Complete these sentences to describe what happened each time.

The higher the voltage of the battery, ______________

The greater the number of batteries, ______________

The longer the wire, ______________

3. The groups needed to make a complete circuit with no breaks. Why?

____

4. What happened at the end of Nigel and Sam's experiment that meant they had to stop? ______________

5. Why did all the pupils draw circuit diagrams using circuit symbols instead of drawing pictures of what they did?

____

6. What problem did Jane and Celia have in their work?

____

Write a set of instructions on another sheet to explain to Nigel and Sam how to carry out Colin, Liz and Peter's experiment. Use some or all of these sentence starters to help you.

Make a circuit using...
Look at the brightness...
Now change...
Look at...

Changing the number of bulbs

These pictures show how to test the effect of changing the number of bulbs on the brightness of each bulb. The pictures have become mixed up. Cut them out and stick them down in the correct order. Then write an instruction to go with each picture. Use the words in the box to help you.

battery cell component crocodile clip
bulb bulb holder wire switch complete
circuit test add observe record

What happens to the brightness of each bulb as more bulbs are added to

the circuit?____

____

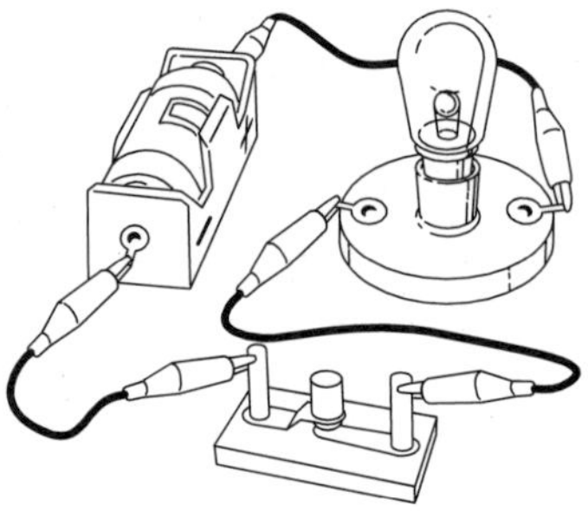

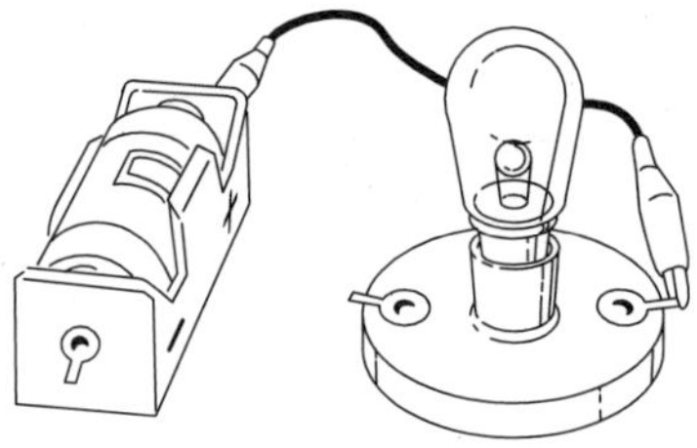

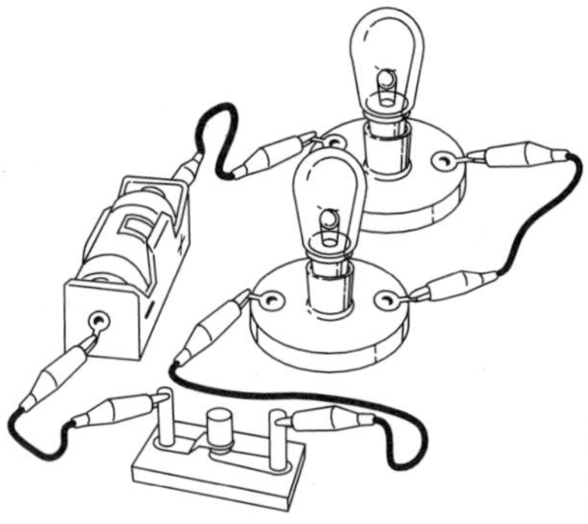

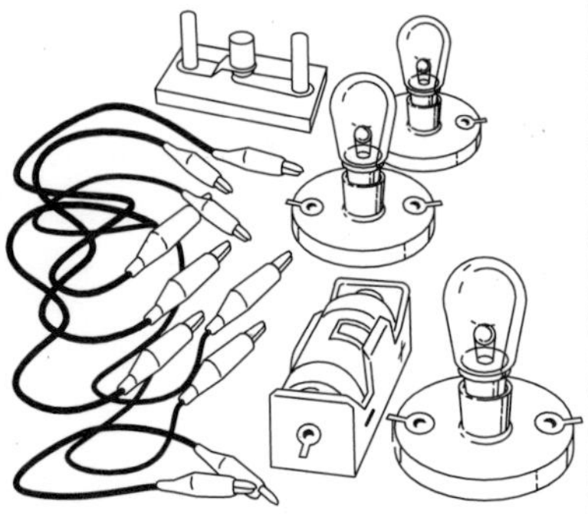

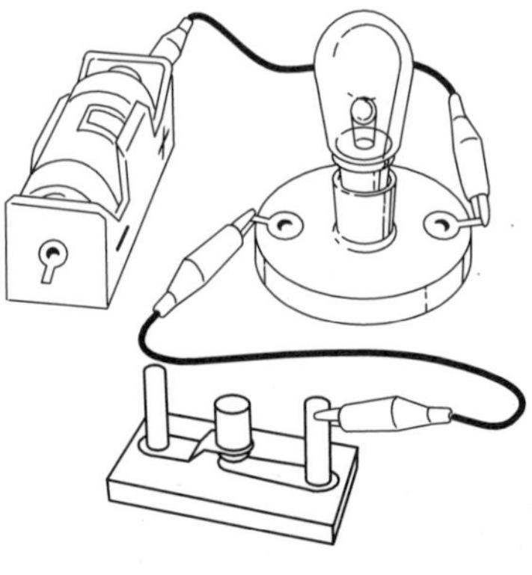

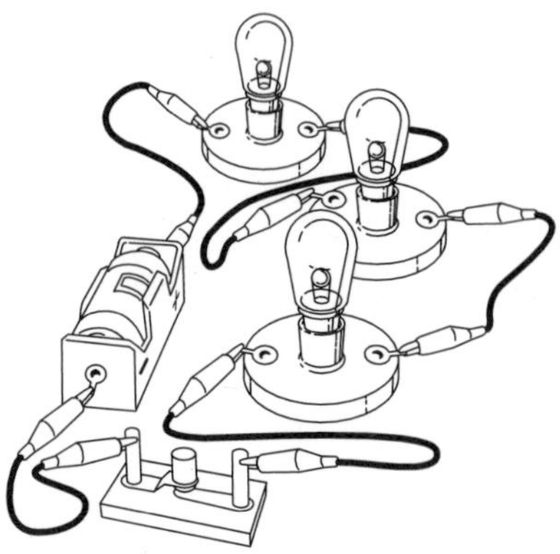

True, false or opinion?

Decide whether each of these statements is true, false or someone's opinion. Write your choice beside each statement and explain your answer.

The greater the voltage of a battery in a circuit, the faster a motor will turn.

Some of the conductors made the bulb light up more brightly.

The longer the length of nichrome wire in a circuit, the brighter the bulb.

Electrical plugs are often made from plastic because plastic is a good electrical conductor.

If your battery has too high a voltage, it can damage the bulb.

Circuit diagrams are easier to understand than pictures.

A buzzer in a circuit containing two cells will be louder than if the circuit contains only one cell.

Only metals conduct electricity.

Adding wire

These pupils were testing what happened to the brightness of a bulb in a circuit when they changed the length of a piece of nichrome wire in the circuit. They used a light sensor connected to a computer to measure the brightness of the bulb.

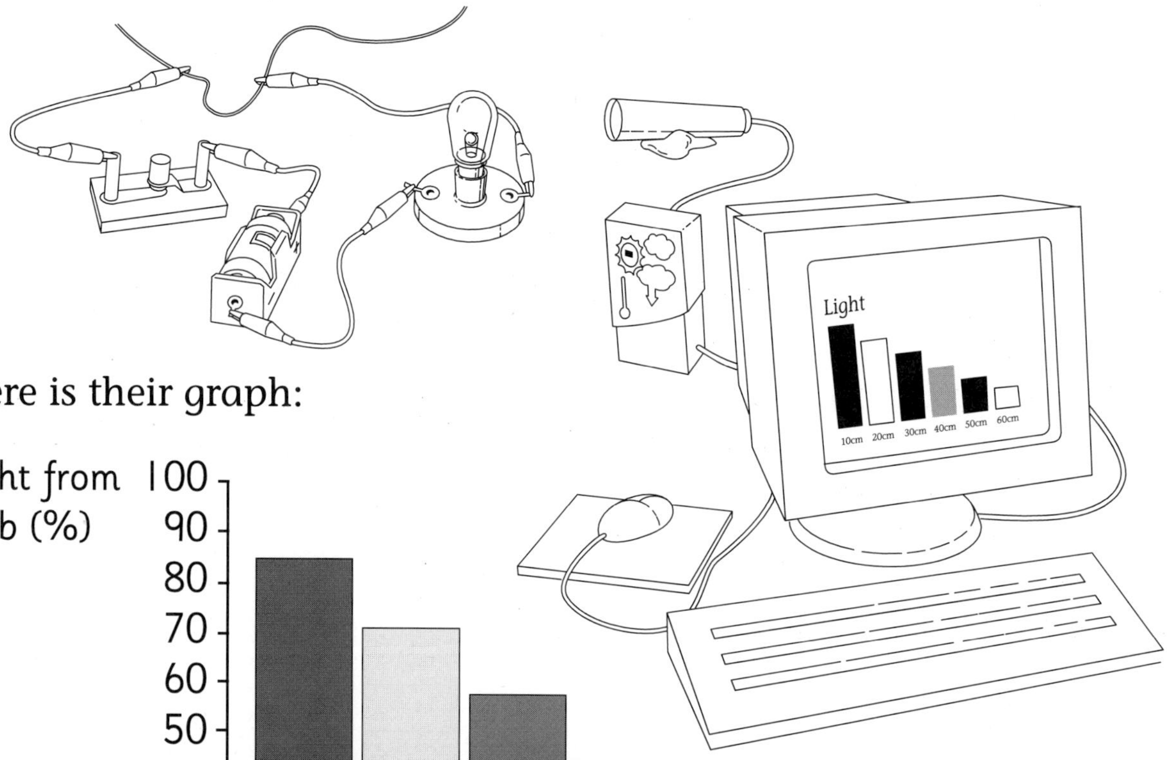

Here is their graph:

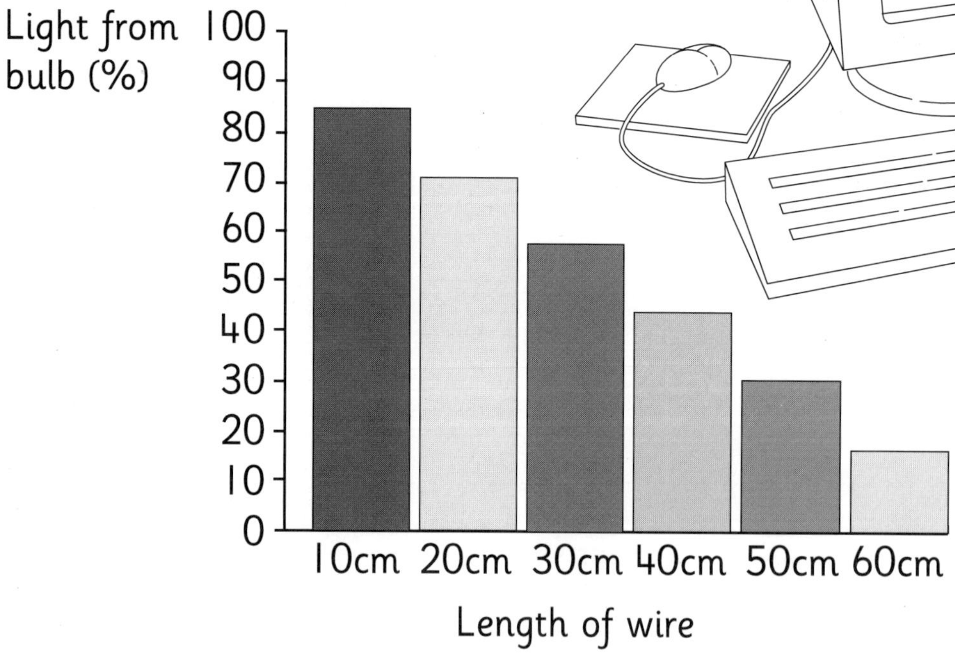

Write a set of questions that you could ask someone else about the experiment. The questions can be about what the pupils did or about their results. Use some of these question starters and some of your own. Then swap questions with a friend and answer each other's questions.

- What did...
- Why did the pupils...
- How did...
- As the length of the wire increased, what...
- How many...

Solving problems

This picture shows some Christmas tree lights that are powered by batteries. Draw a circuit diagram in the box below to show this circuit.

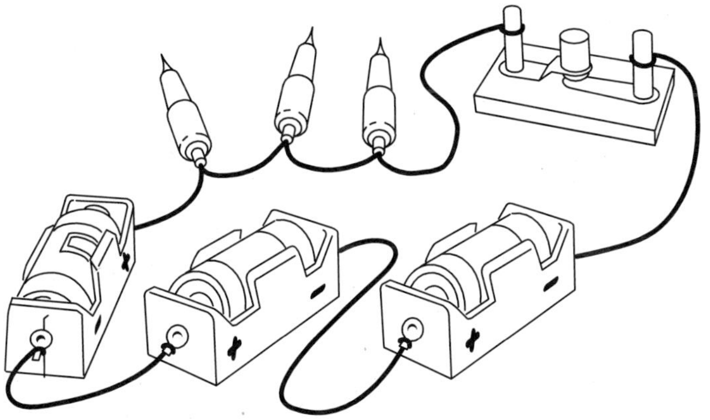

For each of the pictures below, explain why the lights won't work and draw the circuit diagram.

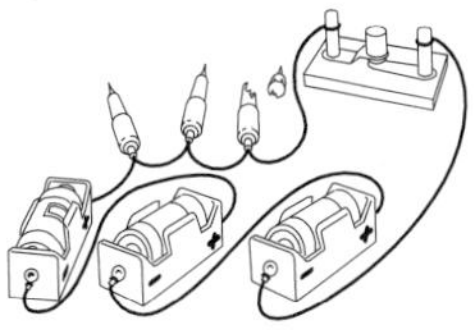

1.

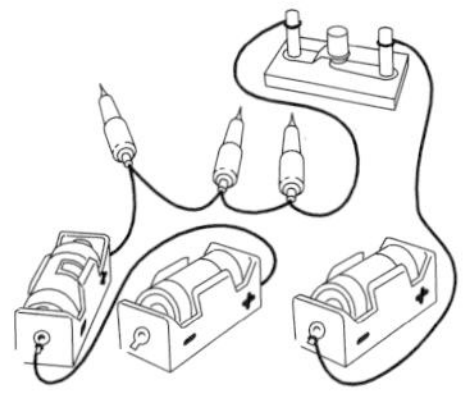

2.

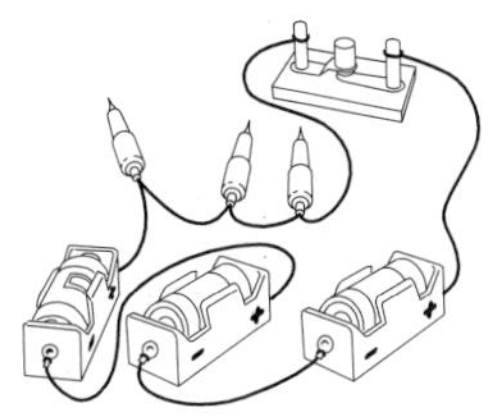

3.

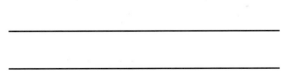

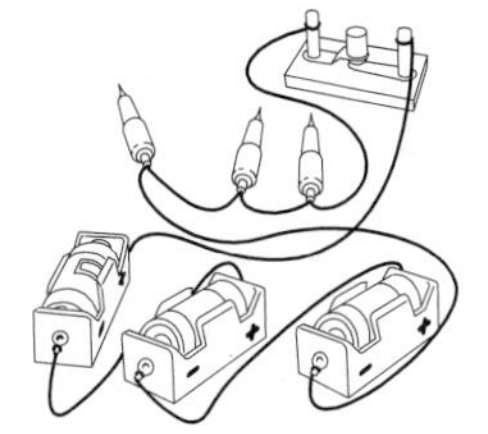

4.

Changing circuits concept map

Join pairs of words together with a line. Write on each line why you have joined those words. One pair has already been done for you. You can use each word more than once.

insulator

bulb

conductor

complete circuit

A complete circuit has no breaks.

brightness

circuit

overload

short circuit

circuit symbol

break

circuit diagram

cell

battery

motor

buzzer

wire

terminals

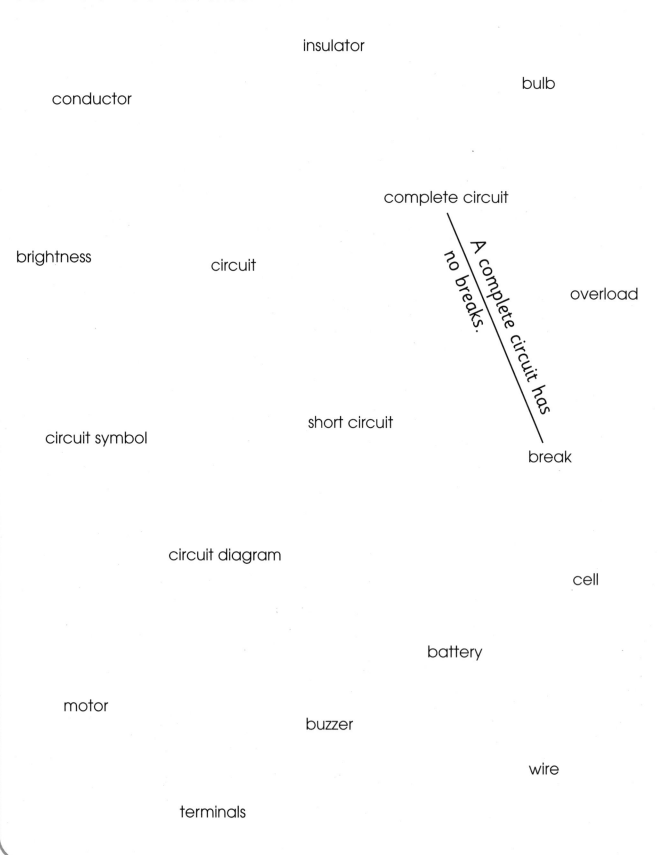

Gravity and air resistance

Here is the writing that a group of pupils did about their investigation into **parachutes**.

Our question: What makes a difference to how long it takes a parachute to **fall**?

What we did: We made parachutes by cutting out circles of material and attaching them to a Blu-tack 'person' with cotton thread. We timed how long they took to fall when we dropped them from a balcony above the hall.

First we tried making parachutes out of different **materials**. We made six parachutes, all the same size, and dropped them from the same place. We used same-sized pieces of Blu-tack and the same length of thread.

Next we tried making parachutes from plastic bags. The bags we used were all from the same supermarket to make the test fair. We cut different-sized circles from the bags. Again, we used the same length of thread and same-sized pieces of Blu-tack. We also dropped them from the same place.

Our predictions: We predicted that when we changed the material of the parachute, there would not be much change in the time it took to fall because all the parachutes were the same size. **Gravity** would make them come **downwards** at a similar speed. We predicted that when we changed the size of the parachute, the **larger** ones would fall more **slowly** because there would be more **air resistance**.

Our results: Different materials

Material	Time to drop (s)
paper towel	6.51
plastic bag	6.23
denim	5.66
net curtain	5.32
card	6.47
hanky	6.34

Plastic bag parachutes

Diameter (cm)	Time to drop (s)
30	8.74
25	7.22
20	6.54
15	4.56
10	3.65
5	2.90

Gravity and air resistance

1. The pupils carried out two separate investigations. What factor did they change each time?

Experiment 1 ______________________________

Experiment 2 ______________________________

2. On another sheet or in your book, explain how they made each investigation a fair test.

3. Draw a line graph using the results the pupils obtained.

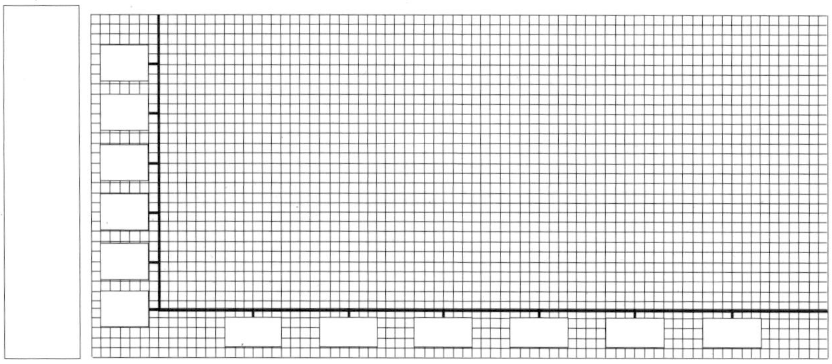

Diameter of parachute (cm)

4. What does the pattern in the graph tell us? The larger the

____

5. The pupils said in their prediction that this would happen because of air resistance. Can you explain what they mean?

____

6. If you had carried out this experiment, which of the measurements would you have chosen to repeat? Why?

____

7. One of the pupils in the group wanted to take three readings for each parachute. What reason is there for doing this?

____

Imagine you are doing a parachute jump. Write about your journey to the ground, using some forces words such as **gravity** and **air resistance**.

Gravity and air resistance

1. What were the pupils trying to find out? Write on another sheet or in your book.

2. They made parachutes out of different materials and tested them. How did they make that a fair test? Write on another sheet.

3. Finish this bar chart, using the results the pupils obtained.

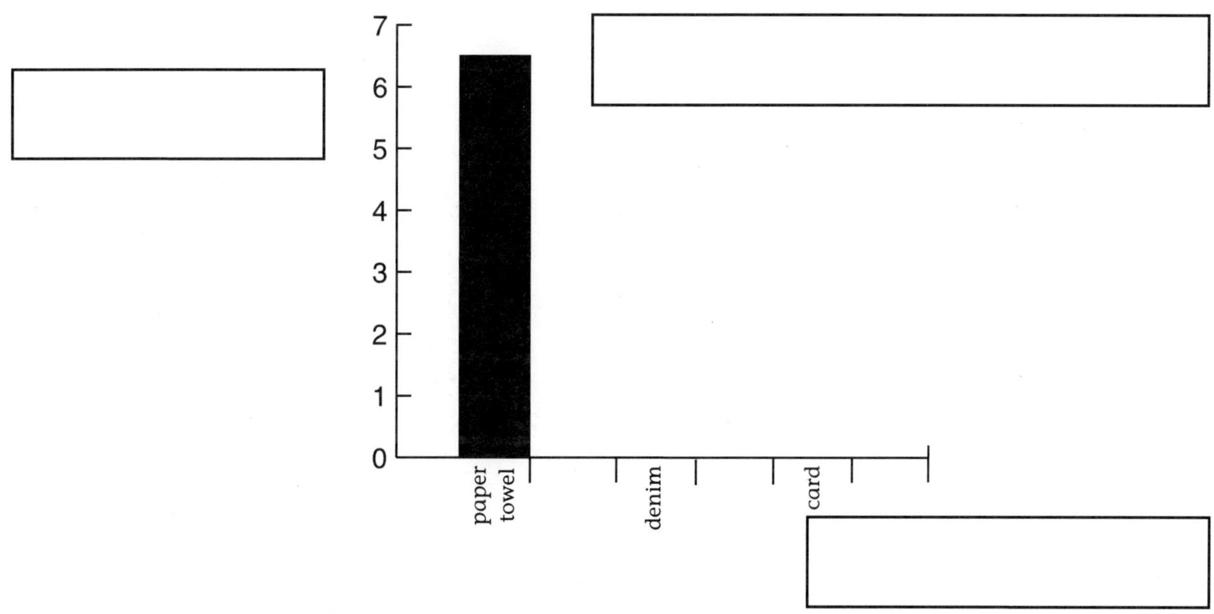

4. After the pupils had tested parachutes made from different materials, they tried another experiment. What did they change this time?

____

5. Here is their graph. What does the pattern in the graph tell us?

The larger the parachute, ______________________________

____

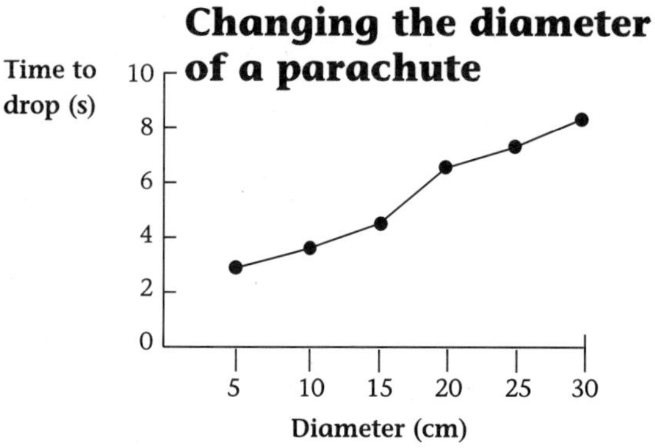

6. In their prediction, the pupils said this would happen because of air resistance. Can you explain what they meant? Write on another sheet.

Imagine you are doing a parachute jump. Write about your journey to the ground, using some forces words such as **gravity** and **air resistance**.

Spot the mistakes

This diagram has been incorrectly labelled. Label the second one correctly.

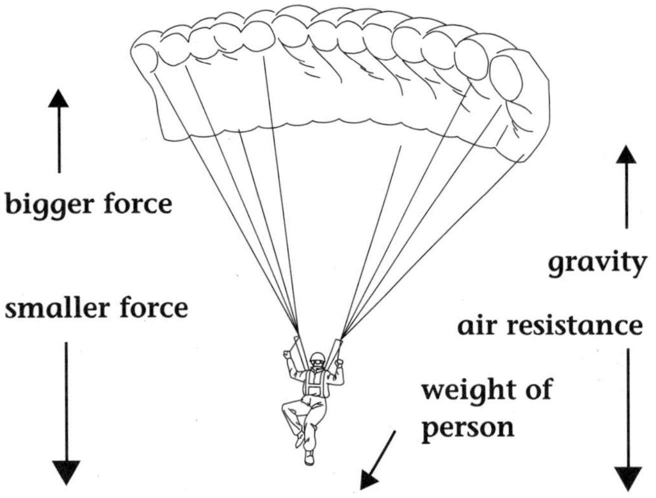

Circle the mistakes in this table. You might need a calculator to help you.

Diameter of parachute (cm)	Time to drop (s)	Mean time to drop (s)
5	2.67 2.45 2.12	2.41
10	3.65 3.66 3.76	3.69
15	4.56 4.68 4.34	4.63
20	6.03 6.10 6.54	6.22
25	7.22 7.43 7.13	21.78
30	8.74 8.84 8.67	8.75

This graph was drawn using a corrected version of the table above. Can you find six mistakes or things left out? List them.

1. ______________________________

2. ______________________________

3. ______________________________

4. ______________________________

5. ______________________________

6. ______________________________

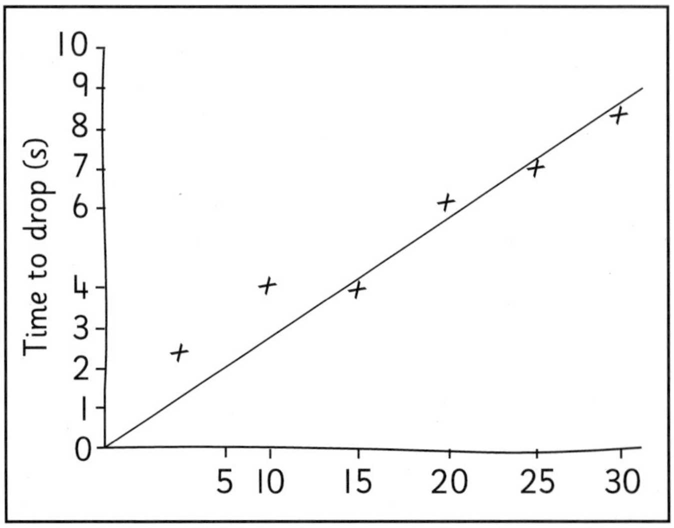

Measuring air resistance

Put these instructions for an experiment on air resistance into the correct order. Your teacher will tell you whether to number the sentences, rewrite them or cut them out and stick them down.

Stretch out the tape measure along the floor, starting at the bottom of the ramp.
Make the front of the vehicle a different shape by adding a card sail or a point made from card. You are trying to make the vehicle either more or less streamlined. This will change its speed. Try several different shapes.
Collect your equipment: you will need a block of wood on wheels, pieces of card and sticky tape, a plank of wood to make a ramp, books, a tape measure, a stopwatch.
Time how long the vehicle takes to run down from the top of the ramp to the end of the tape measure.
Record your results in a table.
Talk about air resistance in your predictions.
Make a ramp on the floor by propping up one end of the plank on a pile of books.
Let the vehicle go down the ramp, first of all without any card attached.
Time the vehicle each time you change the shape of the card attachment.
Each time you change its shape, predict whether the vehicle will go faster or more slowly than the original shape.

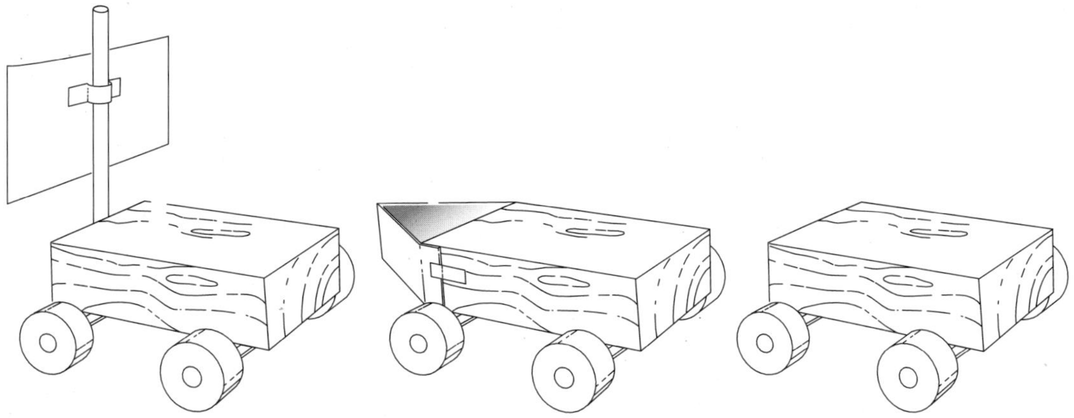

Photocopiable

Gravity and air resistance crossword

Write a clue for each word in the crossword. When you are writing the clues, think about parachute jumps and how you can change the shape of cars to make them go faster.

1 s	t	r	e	2 a	m	l	i	n	i	n	3 g
p				i							r
e				r					4 d		a
e				r					i		v
5 d	e	s	c	e	n	d			s		i
				s					t		t
		6 w	e	i	g	h	t		a		y
				s					n		
				t					c		
	7 p	a	r	a	c	h	u	t	e		
				n							
				c							
				e							

Across

1. ______________________________

____

5. ______________________________

____

6. ______________________________

____

7. ______________________________

____

Down

1. ______________________________

____

2. ______________________________

____

3. ______________________________

____

4. ______________________________

____

Measuring forces

When you **stretch** a rubber band, it gets longer. You use a **pulling force** to stretch it. The more you pull it, the longer it gets. The **harder** you pull it, the tighter it feels on your fingers. It is pulling back into its original shape.

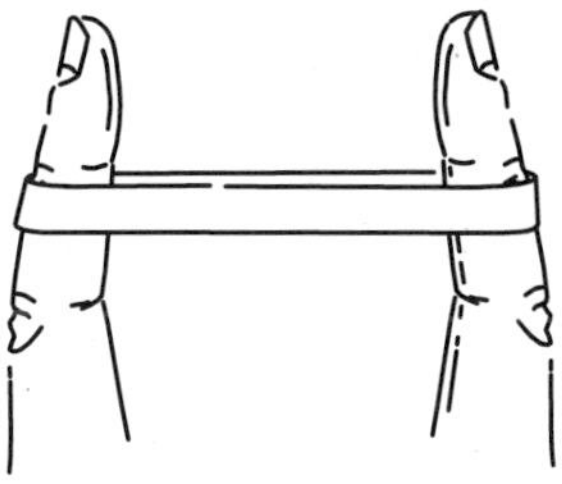

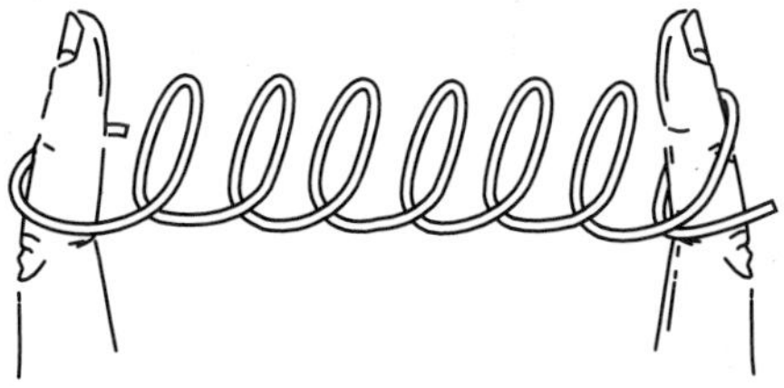

The same thing happens when you pull a **spring**. You can feel the spring pulling on your fingers.

Some springs can be **pushed**. This spring pushes back on your hand when you try to **compress** it. You can feel it pushing back in the **opposite direction** to the way you are pushing it.

Brian can squash a spring like this.

Richard can squash it smaller. He is using a bigger force than Brian. The larger the force, the more the spring is squashed.

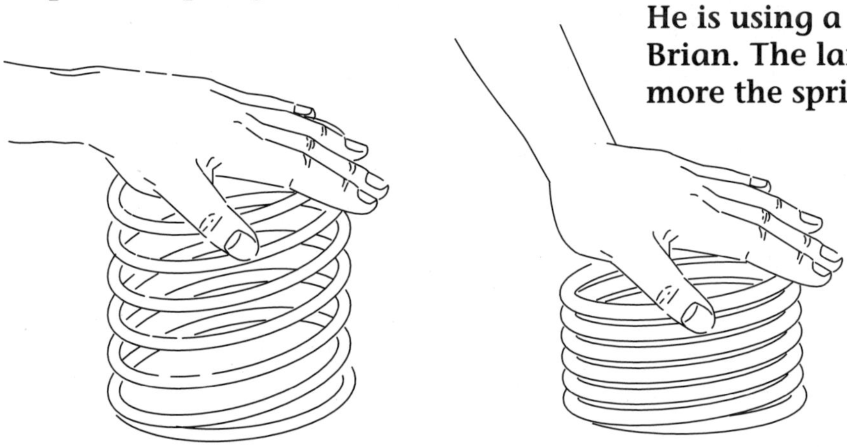

Springs are used inside **force meters**. A force meter measures how strong a force is. Forces are measured in **newtons**. Force meters are sometimes called **newton meters** or **spring balances**.

This person is measuring the force needed to pull a block across a table. It takes 8N (8 newtons) to pull it.

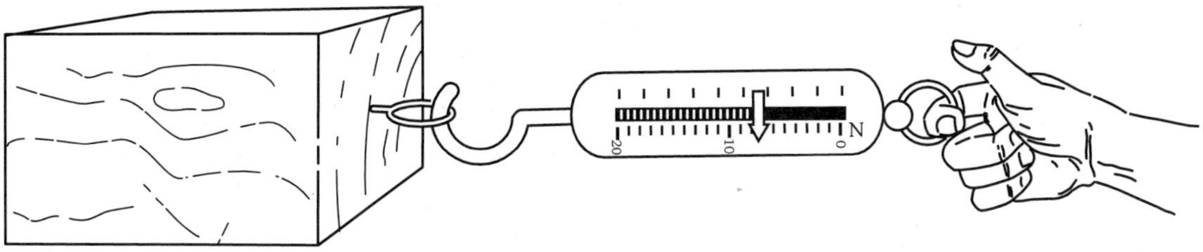

Measuring forces

1. List three things that stretch when they are pulled.

2. Why does a rubber band get tighter when it is pulled?

3. What type of force is used to squash a spring?

4. What happens if a larger force is used to squash the spring?

5. Write down three facts about force meters.

6. Here is another type of force meter. What might be inside the scales to make them work? How would they work?

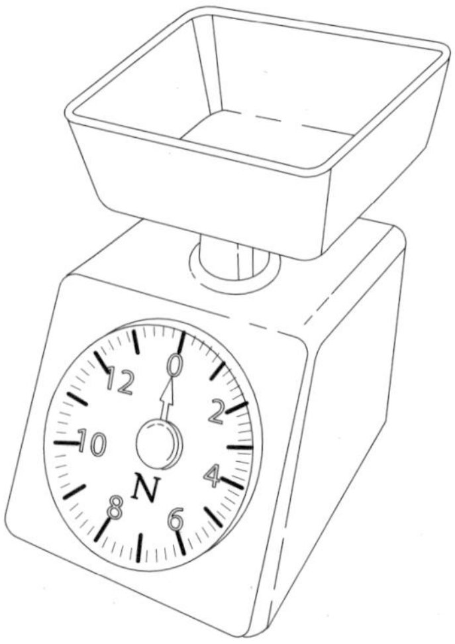

Imagine you are going on a 'forces walk'. You take a big spring with you that can be pulled or pushed. Everything you do on the walk (such as opening or closing a door) must be done with the spring. Write about what happens to the spring.

Measuring forces

1. Name two things that stretch when they are pulled.

_______________ _______________

2. What happens when you stretch a rubber band?

____

3. Why does the rubber band feel tighter on your fingers?

____

4. When you push a spring, what happens to it?

____

5. What can you feel when you push a spring?

____

6. Who used a stronger force on the spring? _______________

How can you tell? _______________

____

7. Write down three facts about force meters.

____

____

____

8. Force meters measure in centimetres. true false

9. Force meters have a rubber band inside. true false

Imagine you are going on a 'forces walk'. You take a big spring with you that can be pulled or pushed. Everything you do on the walk (such as opening or closing a door) must be done with the spring. Write about what happens to the spring.

1 Making force meters

Andrew was stretching a rubber band. He noticed that the harder he pulled it, the longer it became. He decided that he would measure how far the band stretched when it was pulled by different forces. He hung the band on a nail and added masses to it. After 1000g he was worried that the band would snap, so he stopped.

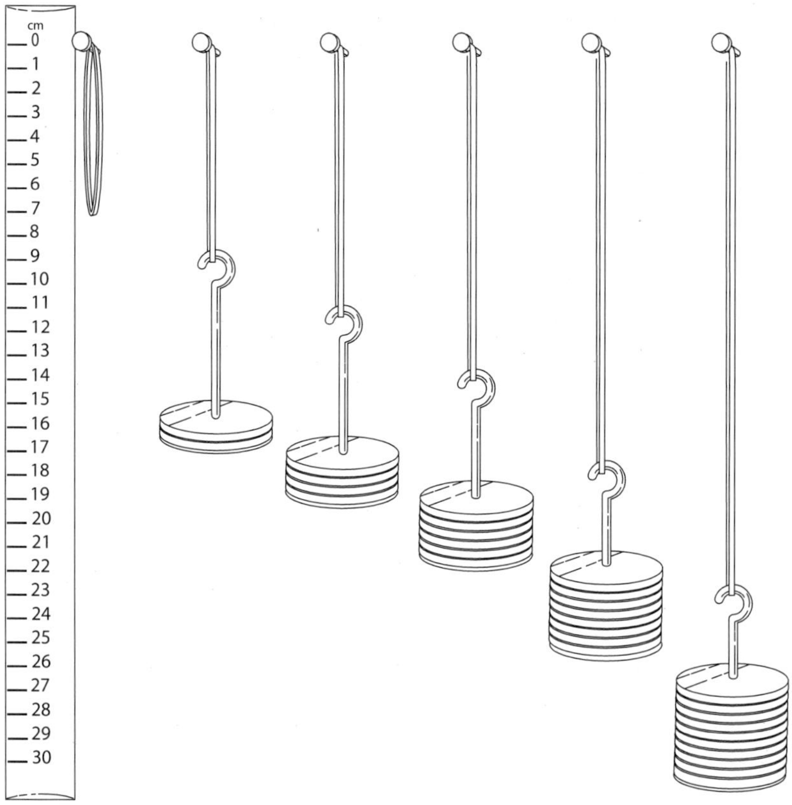

1. How many grams had been added to the rubber band when it stretched by 4cm? ____________

2. How long was the rubber band to begin with? ____________

3. How many different amounts did Andrew add to it? ____________

4. How many times did the rubber band stretch by more than 9cm in total? ____________

5. How many grams had been added when the rubber band stretched to its longest? ____________

6. Each time 200g was added, did the rubber band stretch by the same amount? ____________

7. Why did Andrew stop at 1000g? ____________

____

Making force meters

2

The diagrams below show how to make and use an elastic band force meter. Write instructions for each stage, using the words in the box. Write on another sheet, or in your book. You can use the sentence starters below to help you.

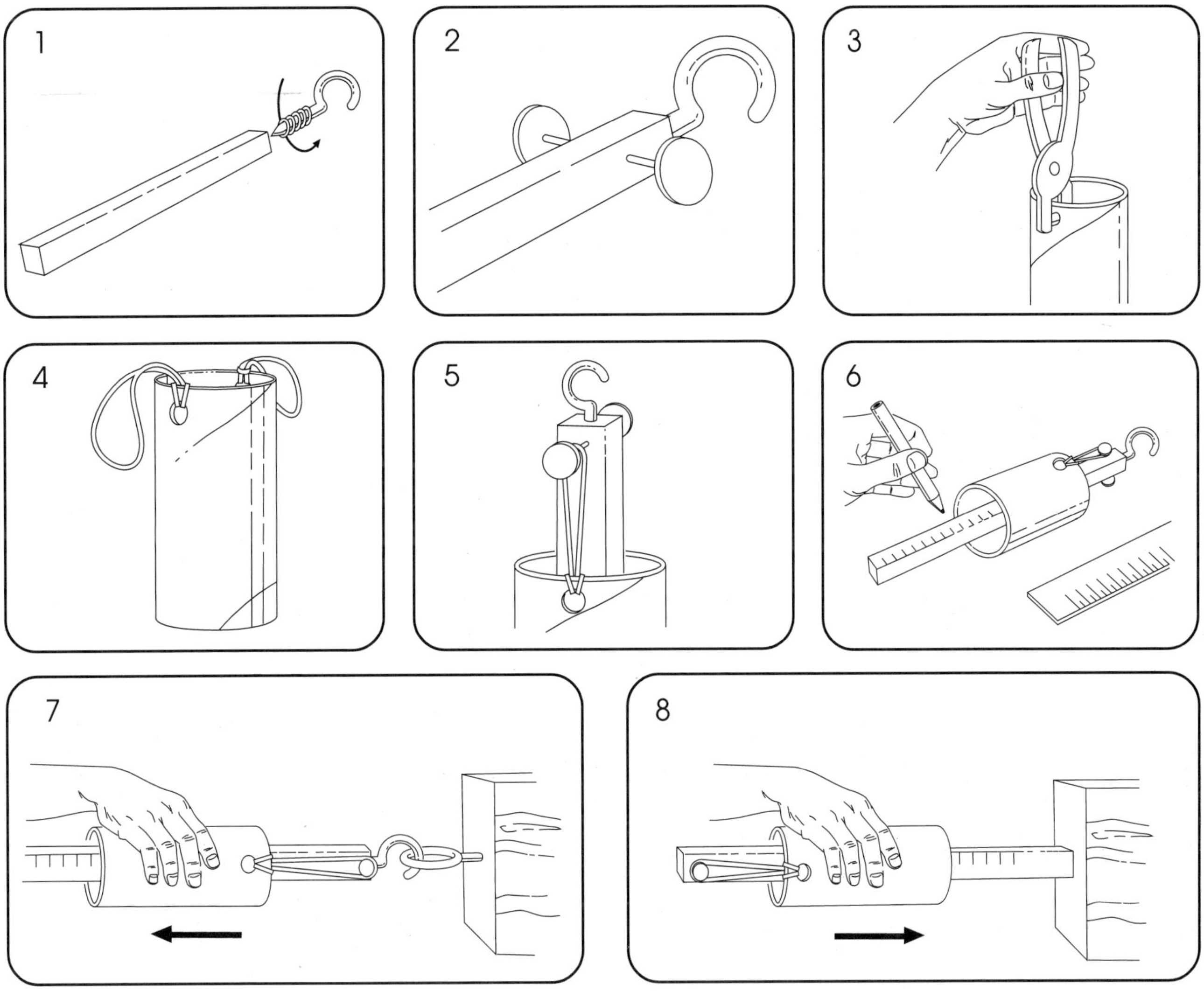

hole punch rubber bands pencil ruler
screw-in hook card tube wooden rod drawing pins
centimetre hold measure mark screw
push pull attach

1. Screw the hook into the end of
2. Push
3. Punch
4. Attach
5. Put
6. Mark
7. Measure pulling forces by
8. Measure pushing

3 Making force meters

The statements below are about using rubber bands or springs to make force meters. Divide them into four lists in a table:

Advantages of springs	Disadvantages of springs	Advantages of rubber bands	Disadvantages of rubber bands

- A rubber band does not stretch evenly.
- If you stretch a spring too far, it will not return to its original shape and size.
- A spring stretches evenly.
- Rubber bands wear out. The rubber can lose its stretchiness and become hard and brittle.
- Rubber bands are cheap.
- Rubber bands can snap suddenly.
- A spring goes back to its original shape and size time after time.
- A spring can rust if it gets wet.
- A rubber band does not always go back exactly to its original length after stretching.

Underline the statements that you think are most important when deciding whether to use a spring or a rubber band to make a force meter.

Would you choose a spring or a rubber band if you were making a force meter? Explain your choice. ____________________

____

____

____

Measuring the strength of magnets

Write labels to explain what is happening in the picture. Use the words in the box to help you.

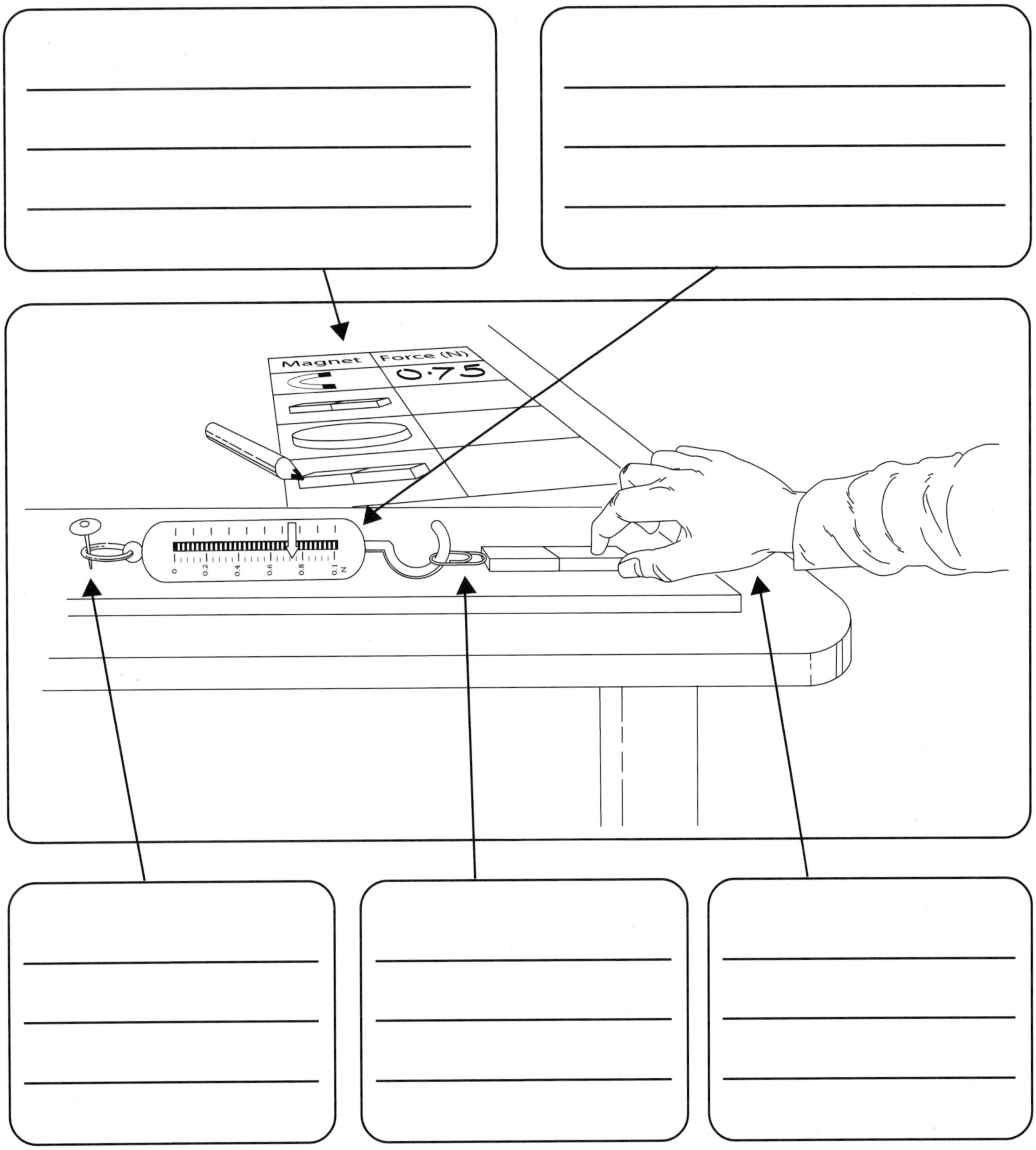

best strongest compare strength attracted results
force meter paper clip hook pulling force
newtons scale read measure magnet
table record nail

Measuring forces card game

Teacher instructions
Photocopy onto card. Cut along the dotted lines. Fold each card in half along the solid line, with the text on the outside, and fasten with adhesive tape. If you are working with a small group, give each child a card. If you are working with the whole class, share the cards out one between two or three. All the cards must be given out.

The child (or group) with the card marked * reads the question aloud. The child (or group) with the answer to that question reads out the answer, then reads out the question on the back of that card. This goes on until the first child (or group) has read out the answer on the first card.

Q * A pull or a push is a ________.	**A** measure forces
Q If you pull this, it will stretch unevenly.	**A** force
Q An instrument to measure forces.	**A** a rubber band
Q There is one of these inside a force meter.	**A** a force meter
Q A force meter measures in these units.	**A** a spring
Q A force meter measures the ________ of a force.	**A** newtons
Q The harder you pull a spring…	**A** strength
Q You can get bathroom scales that measure in newtons. They measure ________ forces.	**A** the longer it becomes
Q Most force meters measure ________ forces.	**A** pushing
Q If you push something, you can feel it pushing back in the…	**A** pulling
Q Force meters are sometimes called…	**A** opposite direction
Q Newton meters and spring balances are other names for force meters. They are used to…	**A** newton meters or spring balances

Forces in action

When an object is placed in water, it will either **float** or **sink**. Whether it floats or sinks depends on the **forces** acting on it. The force of the object's **weight** pulls it down. This force is caused by **gravity**. A force called **upthrust** from the water pushes it up.

If you try to push a table-tennis ball down into a bowl of water, you can feel the upthrust from the water pushing in the **opposite** direction. If you let go of the ball, it bounces up to the surface of the water.

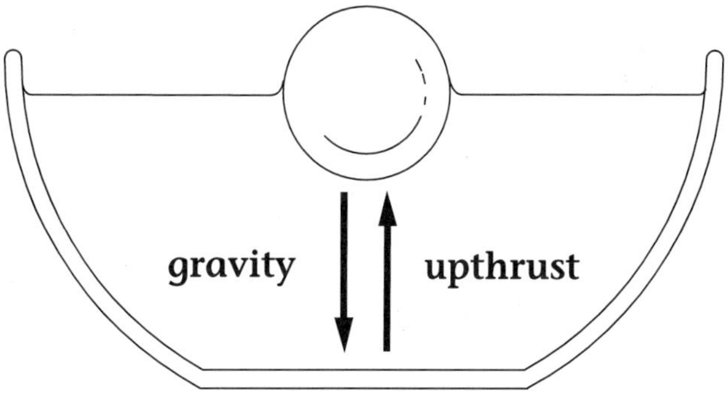

If you put a marble into a bowl of water, it will sink. This is not just because the marble is **heavier** than the table-tennis ball. Whether an object floats depends on its size as well as how heavy it is. A lump of Plasticine will sink in water – but if you make it into a hollow boat shape, it will float. The Plasticine boat will float because it is less heavy for its size than the lump.

Solid materials that are heavy for their size include glass, most metals and some plastics. These materials usually sink in water. Solid materials that are **lighter** for their size include wood, polystyrene and cork. These materials usually float.

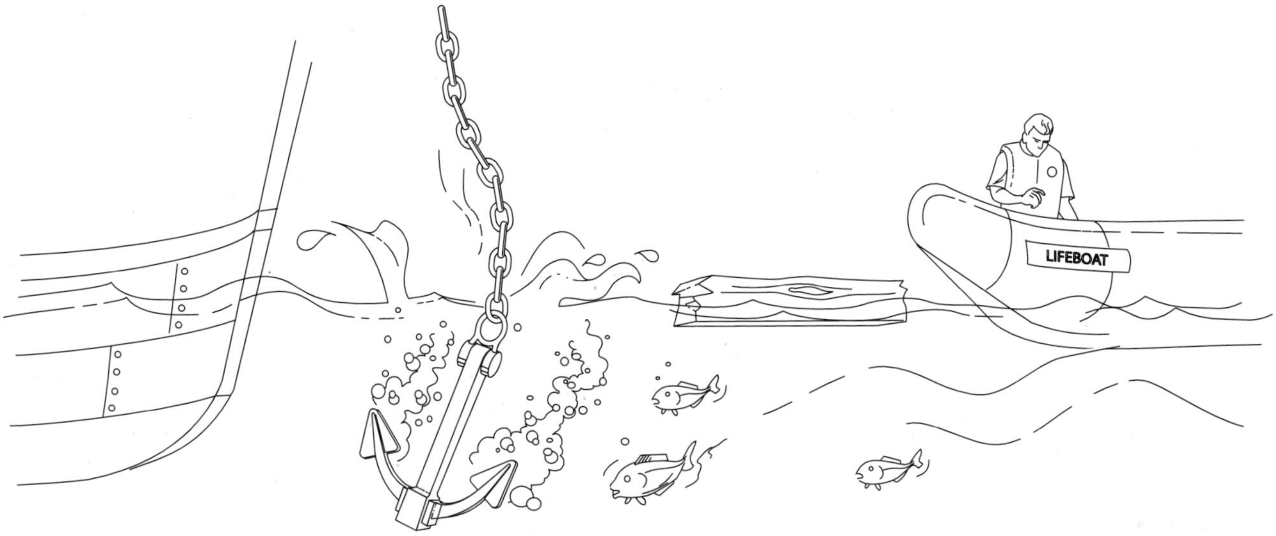

Forces in action

1. Name the two forces acting on an object in water.

_______________________ _______________________

2. In which directions do these two forces act?

_______________________ _______________________

3. Why does a boat made of steel float in water, when a flat piece of steel with the same mass sinks?

____

____

4. Write two lists of objects: things that float on water and things that sink.

Float	Sink

5. How could you make a table-tennis ball sink without pushing it down in the water?____

____

Air resistance and upthrust are both forces that can push upwards. Look in books about forces to find out the difference between air resistance and upthrust. Draw labelled diagrams to show the difference.

Forces in action

1. What force causes an object to sink? ______________________

2. What force causes an object to float? ______________________

3. In which direction do these two forces act?

   Upthrust ______________________

   Gravity ______________________

4. Give an example from the text of an object that floats and an object that sinks.

____________________________________ ____________________________________

5. Why will a hollow boat made of Plasticine float when a ball of Plasticine will sink? ____

____

6. Write two lists of objects: things that will float in water and things that will sink.

Float	Sink
______________	______________
______________	______________
______________	______________
______________	______________
______________	______________
______________	______________

Air resistance and upthrust are both forces that can push upwards. Look in books about forces to find out the difference between air resistance and upthrust. Draw labelled diagrams to show the difference.

Floating and sinking poems

Writing a poem about a word can help you to remember the word, its meaning and how it is spelled.

Upthrust	One word – the word you want to remember.
Pushes up	Two words – what the first word means, or something it does.
Works in water	Three words – what it does, its function or its effect.
Helps me to swim	Four words – how you feel about it.
Floating	One word – a word that helps you to remember the first word.

Try writing poems like that for these words:

Gravity

______ ______

______ ______ ______

______ ______ ______ ______

______

Sinking

______ ______

______ ______ ______

______ ______ ______ ______

______

Try these other forces words: air resistance, friction, force meter, newton.

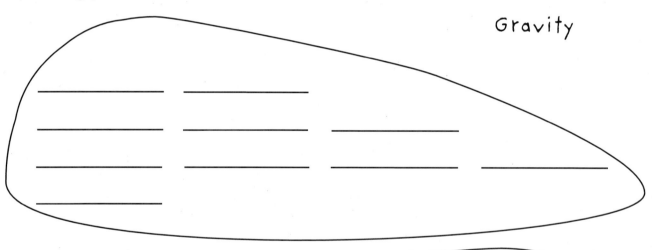

Forces in action picture words

Sometimes it's easier to remember the spelling or meaning of a word by drawing a picture word.

For example:

Try to make a picture word using each of these words:

force	air resistance	spring balance
heavy	light	push
pull	friction	stretch

Forces in action summary

Read these two paragraphs. Underline the sentences that are **describing** forces. Use a highlighter pen or yellow crayon to highlight the sentences that are giving an **explanation**.

Hint: an explanation gives a reason why something happens.

Floating and sinking
When an object is placed in water, usually it will sink to the bottom or float on the top. If it sinks, this is because the force of its weight (caused by gravity) is stronger than the force of upthrust from the water acting on it. Objects that float in water do so because they are not very heavy for their size.

Dropping things
The reason an object falls when it is dropped from a height is that gravity pulls it downwards towards the Earth. Sometimes objects don't fall down quickly, but float down gently. This is not just because they are light, but because of air resistance pushing upwards and slowing their descent. Two identical sheets of paper, one kept flat and one crumpled-up into a ball, fall at different speeds. The crumpled up sheet of paper falls more quickly because it has less air resistance acting on it.

Friction
Describe what is happening in the picture.
Do **not** give an explanation.

____

____

____

Now give an **explanation** of what is happening, using the word

'friction'. ____

____

____

Forces and scientists

1

Ideas about forces have developed gradually. The history of the idea of gravity has involved many scientists. In earlier times, people wondered about the Sun and the stars, but they did not know what these bodies were or how the Solar System worked. The first astronomical records were made in China around 1000 BC.

Aristotle (384–322BC), a Greek, believed that the Earth was at the centre of the universe, with crystal spheres around it to keep the planets and stars in place. He thought the gods pushed the spheres around. This was before anyone had thought of gravity, and about a hundred years before Archimedes shouted 'Eureka!' when he realised that upthrust acts on floating objects. Another Greek scientist, a woman named Hypatia (AD370–415), invented an instrument to measure the positions of the Sun, stars and planets.

In AD813 a School of Astronomy was opened in Baghdad. In Germany, a nun named Hildegard (1098–1179), drew maps of the universe based on Aristotle's ideas. Jean Buridan (1300–1385), a French scientist, decided that gods couldn't possibly be pushing the stars around, and suggested that God had started them off to move at a steady speed for ever. Late in the lifetime of a Polish monk called Copernicus (1473–1543), he suggested that the Earth travelled around the Sun. An Italian, Galileo Galilei (1564–1642), agreed with him, but was threatened with torture for his beliefs.

Later, Johannes Kepler (1571–1630) suggested that the planets travelled at different speeds around the Sun. This was confirmed by an Englishman, Isaac Newton (1642–1727), who developed a theory of gravity. Newton also described 'laws' of force and movement that we now take for granted. He explained what happens if an object is not pushed or pulled at all, what effects forces have, and why you feel an opposing push from an object when you push it. Newton's theory that all objects exert a force of gravity is very important for modern scientists, and our unit of force is named after him.

2

Forces and scientists

Use the information on the sheet 'Forces and scientists 1' to help you complete this table.

Scientist	Born	Died	Nationality	Discovery, theory or invention

Changing pitch

These pupils were carrying out investigations into a variety of sound-makers. They were trying to find out what factors affect **pitch**. Pitch is how **low** or **high** a sound is.

David M and Paul

We used a guitar. The **strings vibrated** to produce the sound. We found that the **thinner** strings made **higher** sounds and the **thicker** strings made **lower** sounds. In fact, the **thicker** the string, the **lower** the sound was.

John and Julian

We used milk bottles in our experiment. We blew across the tops of the bottles to make the air inside **vibrate**. We put some water in the bottles so that there was a different amount of air in each bottle. We noticed that the more air there was in the bottle, the **lower** the sound was.

Stuart and Vimty

We used milk bottles to make sounds. We filled them with different amounts of water and tapped them with a stick. We found that the more water there was inside the bottle, the **lower** the sound was. The water was **vibrating**.

Ranjit and Sue M

We used a guitar and looked at one string. We changed the **tension** of the string. We started with the string quite loose, and then we **tightened** it using the **tuning** peg. As the string became **tighter**, the sound became **higher**.

Sajida and Noreen

We used a ruler to make a sound. We held it on the edge of the desk and 'twanged' it. The **shorter** the **vibrating** part of the ruler, the **higher** the sound was. It seemed to vibrate faster when it was shorter.

Changing pitch

1. What does the word **pitch** mean?

____

2. How did David M and Paul change the pitch in their investigation?

____

3. What did they find out?

____

4. Another group used a guitar. What did this group find out?

____

____

5. Two groups used milk bottles to make sounds.
What was vibrating in Stuart and Vimty's investigation, and what did they discover?____

____

What was vibrating in John and Julian's investigation, and what did they discover?____

____

6. What was discovered about the vibrations in the investigation with the ruler?____

____

Choose either A or B:

A Choose a sound-maker that is **not** mentioned on the 'Changing pitch' sheet, such as a violin, drum or recorder. Describe how to change the pitch of its sound.

B Choose one of the experiments from the text and draw a diagram to show what the children did.

Changing pitch

1. What does the word **pitch** mean?

____

2. How did David M and Paul change the pitch in their investigation?

What did they find out?

The thicker the string,

3. What did Ranjit and Sue M find out?

The tighter the string,

4. What was vibrating in Stuart and Vimty's investigation?______

What did they find out?

The more water in the bottle,

5. How did John and Julian make sounds with their milk bottles, and what did they find out?______

____

____

6. What did Sajida and Noreen find out?______

____

____

Choose either A or B:

A Choose a sound-maker that is **not** mentioned on the 'Changing pitch' sheet, such as a violin, drum or recorder. Describe how to change the pitch of its sound.

B Choose one of the experiments from the text and draw a diagram to show what the children did.

Oboestraws

Here is the writing that a group of pupils did about some instruments they made. Write a set of instructions to help a group of pupils in your class make and test 'oboestraws' for themselves.

Question: How can we change the pitch of an oboestraw?

Apparatus: We used art straws (paper straws) and scissors.

Method: We cut the art straws to different lengths. We squashed one end of each straw so it was flat. Then we cut this end to a point.

We squashed the two pointed bits together gently, and put this end in our mouths. We made sure our lips were dry, so we didn't dampen the straw. We pushed the straw a couple of centimetres into our mouths and blew into it to make a sound.

Observations: When we blew, the straws made different sounds. In general, the longer the straw, the lower the sound was – but it also depended on how hard we blew. Some of our group could not make any sound with the straws. They might have been blowing too hard.

Rubber band jazz

Here are some instructions for making different-pitched sounds with a rubber band. They have become mixed up. Cut them out and stick them in the correct order.

Now stretch the rubber band a bit more and try again.

Gently stretch the rubber band away from your ear with your other hand.

Listen again to hear how the pitch has changed.

Press down, so your ear is 'closed'.

Hold one end of a rubber band to the middle of your ear.

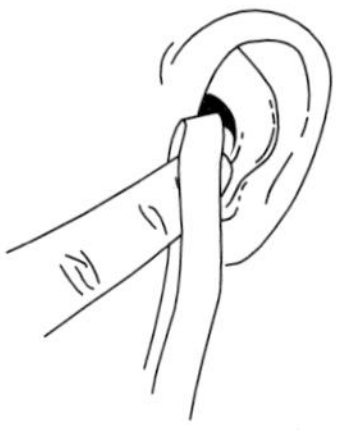

Use a free finger to pluck the rubber band.

Listen carefully to the sound.

Be careful not to let go – it could hurt!

Pitch relationships

Complete these 'relationship sentences' about musical instruments and other sound-makers. Each sentence will end with either **...the higher the sound** or **...the lower the sound**.

The longer the vibrating part of the string of a guitar, ______

The tighter the string of a guitar, ______

The thicker the string of a violin, ______

The tighter the skin of a drum, ______

The looser the string of a guitar, ______

The quicker the vibrations of a tuning fork, ______

The shorter the length of a 'twanged' ruler, ______

The longer the tube that you blow across, ______

The longer the prongs of a tuning fork, ______

The tighter a rubber band is stretched, ______

Now write two of your own 'relationship sentences' about pitch.

______

______

______

______

The band begins to play...

Read this passage about a band. Draw the table below in your book or on paper. Use the information in the passage to complete the table. You should be able to include four facts about high sounds and four facts about low sounds. Try not to copy sentences from the passage.

Each member of the band has a different instrument to play. The percussion player makes high sounds by hitting the shorter tubes of steel, and low sounds by hitting the longer tubes. The drummer uses the biggest drums to make the lowest sounds. Guitar players can make low sounds with the thickest strings on their instruments. To make higher sounds, they either use thinner strings or shorten the length of the string that is vibrating. The flute player makes quite high notes most of the time, and so does the violin player. The double bass player uses a bow to make the strings vibrate like violin strings, but the sounds produced are much lower than those from a violin.

High sounds	Low sounds

Changing pitch crossword

Write a clue, using the theme of pitch, for each of the words in this crossword.

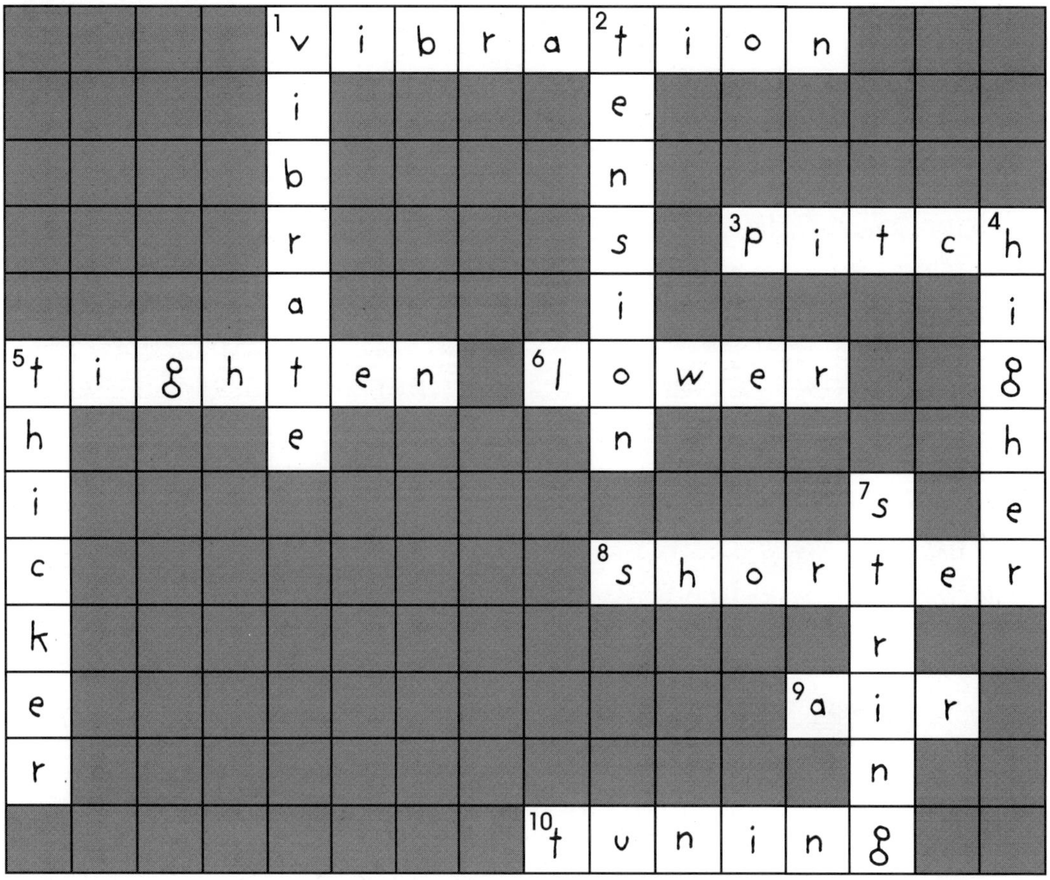

Across

1. ______________________

3. ______________________

5. ______________________

6. ______________________

8. ______________________

9. ______________________

10. ______________________

Down

1. ______________________

2. ______________________

4. ______________________

5. ______________________

7. ______________________

Loud and quiet

Loud sounds are easy to hear. They can sometimes be unpleasant. Very loud sounds can damage your **ears**.

Some people work in places where there is a lot of loud **noise**. Places such as airports, building sites and some factories can be very noisy. In these workplaces, the workers often wear **earmuffs** to **muffle** the sound. The materials in the earmuffs block out some of the sound and make it seem **quieter**. In this way, the workers' ears are protected from the **loudness** of the sounds around them.

In some workplaces, it is important that there is complete **silence**. In a radio or television studio, only the sounds wanted for the programme should be recorded. Think about your classroom: when it is quiet, can you hear people talking in the corridor or the next room? If television studios were like that, you might hear someone discussing their plans for the weekend while the news was on. To prevent this, the studios are **soundproofed**. Special materials are used in the walls, floor and ceiling, and even on the doors, to **muffle** sounds from outside.

'Tomorrow the Prime Minister will be ...'
'...buying some shelves and a new fish-tank.'

Loud and quiet

1. What are the problems with very loud sounds? ________________

2. How can people who work in noisy places protect themselves?

3. How do earmuffs work? ________________

4. Explain why television studios need to be soundproofed.

5. Describe how a studio is made soundproof. ________________

6. Name three other places where soundproofing would be useful.

7. Explain why the soundproofing would be useful in these places.

Listen carefully for one minute to the sounds around you. Write a list of all the sounds in order of loudness, starting with the quietest.

Loud and quiet

1. Loud sounds can damage ______________________________

2. Why do people who work in noisy places wear earmuffs?

____

____

3. How do earmuffs protect your ears? ______________________________

____

____

4. Why does it need to be silent in a television recording studio?

____

____

5. What do they do in television recording studios to muffle the sounds from outside? ______________________________

____

____

6. Suggest another place where soundproofing would be useful.

____

7. Why would soundproofing be useful in this place?

____

____

____

Listen carefully for one minute to the sounds around you. Write a list of all the sounds in order of loudness, starting with the quietest.

Making and testing earmuffs

These diagrams show how a group of pupils made and tested earmuffs. Use the words in the box to help you write a description of each diagram.

sound loud scissors drop measure
cover pin quiet fabrics further
materials repeat thickness ears
tape measure hear move record

1

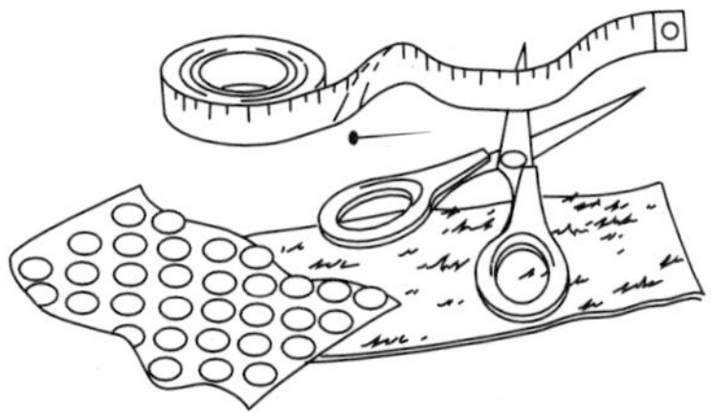

2

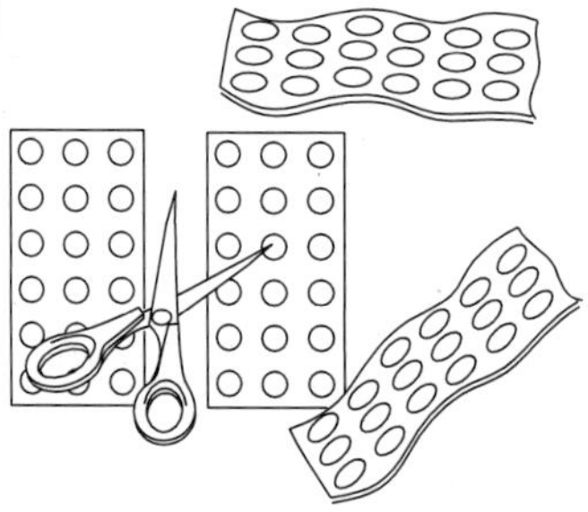

3

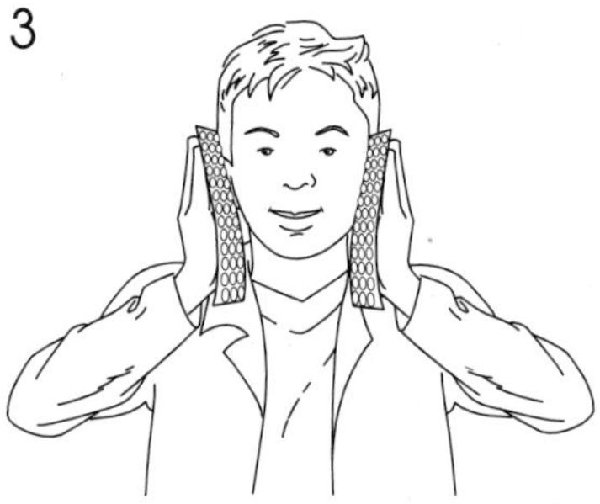

4

5

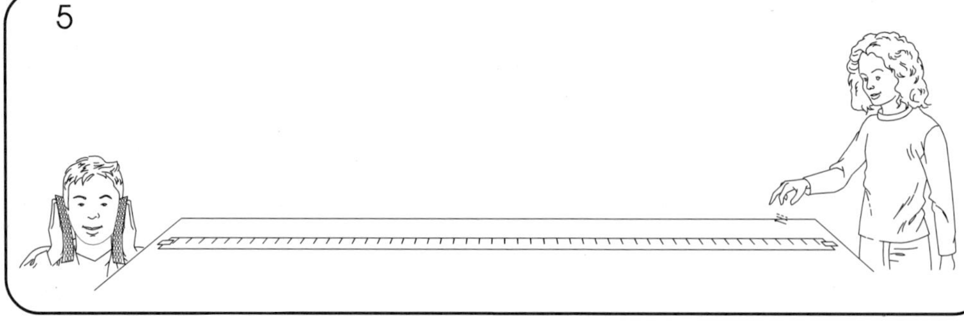

6

Material	*Distance at which pin drop could no longer be heard*

7

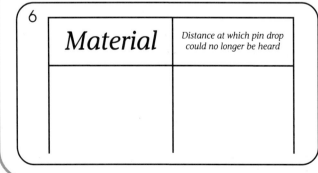

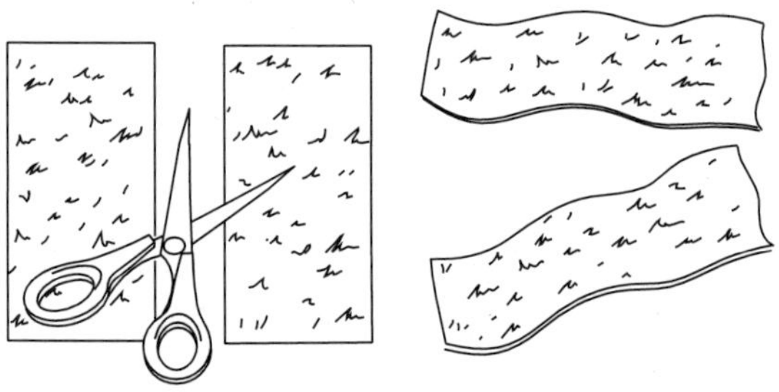

Sensing sound

A group of pupils used a sound sensor to measure the sound level outside their school. They produced a graph on their computer to show the sound level over 14 hours.

To complete the key below, match the labels to the correct points on the graph by writing the correct letters in the boxes.

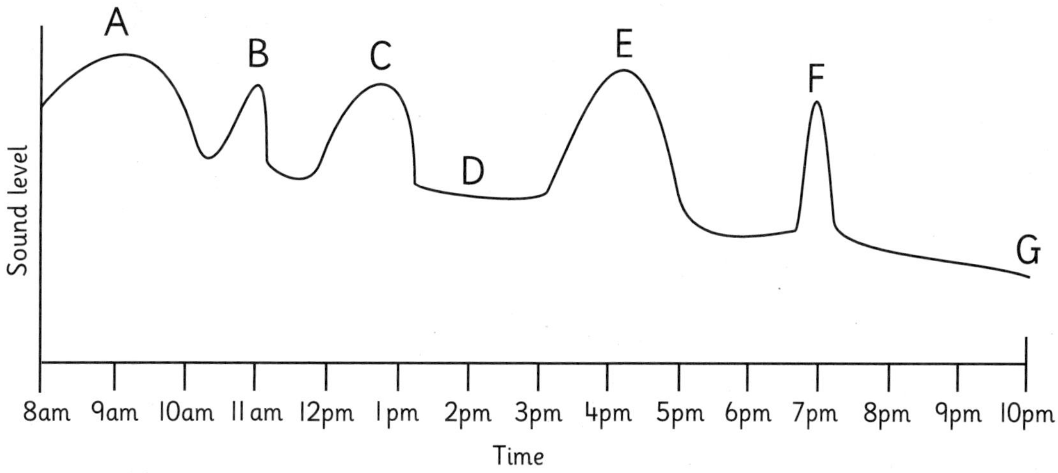

KEY

- Lots of noise from cars and parents picking up children. ☐
- The noise level is high because children are being dropped off for school. ☐
- The quietest time. Very few cars are passing by. ☐
- School lunchtime. Children in the playground cause an increase in the sound level. ☐
- The football team come back from a match. They have won. Their cheers cause an increase in the sound level. ☐
- Morning break means a rise in the noise level outside the school. ☐
- No pupils are outside. Only an average number of cars are passing by. ☐

Try to imagine what the sound level graph would look like for your classroom over 24 hours. Sketch the graph and label it.

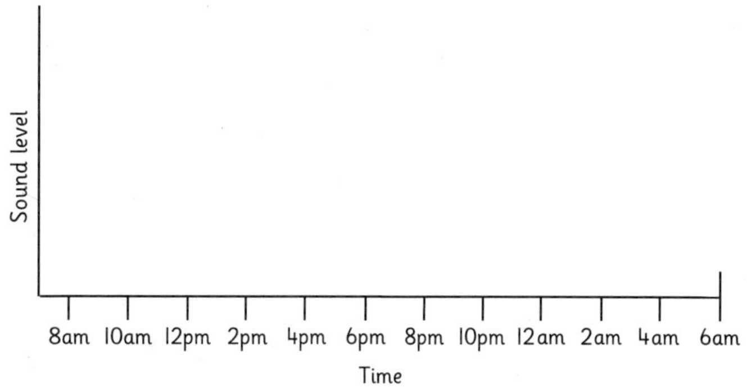

Sound concept map

Join pairs of words together with a line. Write on each line why you have joined those words. One pair has already been done for you. You can use each word more than once.

pitch

muffle

tuning

loud

ears

noise

soundproof

short

sound

quiet

high — thin strings make high sounds — thin string

vibration

tight string

low

thick string

long

loudness

loose string

Shadows

A **shadow** is caused when an **opaque object blocks** the **light** from a source. Because **light travels** in **straight lines**, it cannot get around an opaque object.

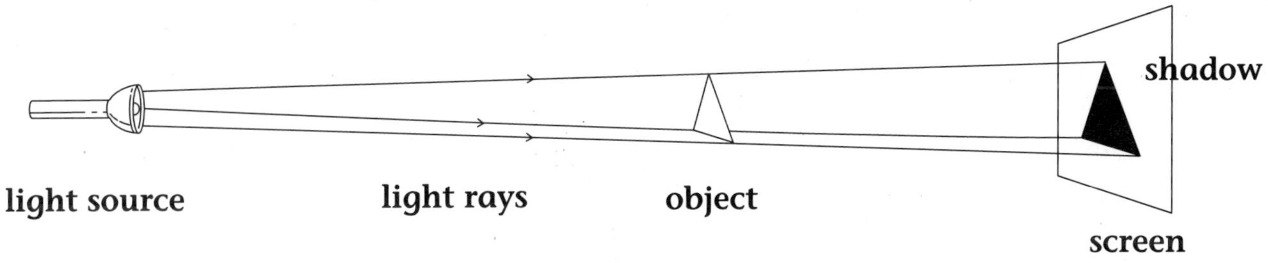

There are a number of ways to change a shadow.

If you move the **light source** closer to the object, the shadow becomes larger.

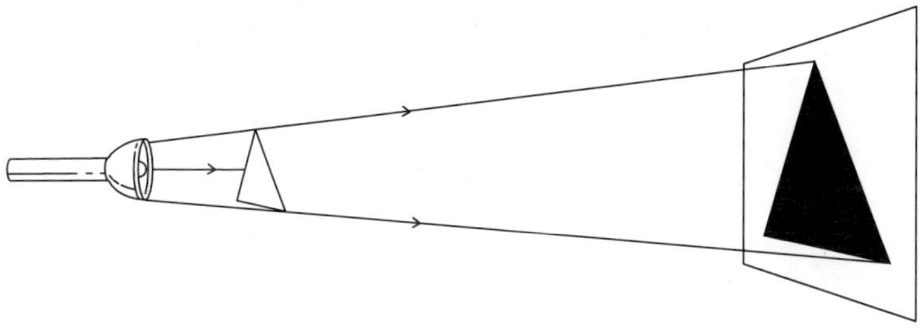

If you move the object further away from the light source, the shadow becomes smaller again.

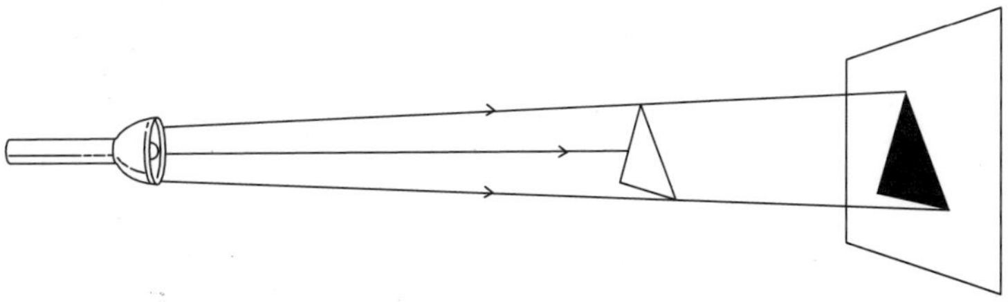

Changing the **position** of the **screen** also affects the size of the shadow. Changing the **angle** of the light source can make the shadow longer or shorter. Changing the type or size of the light source can make the shadow **sharper** or **fuzzier**.

Changing the shape or size of the object will change the shadow. Also, the material from which the object is made can affect the shadow: an **opaque** material blocks the light to make a very dark shadow, a **translucent** object lets a little light through to make a faint shadow, but a **transparent** object doesn't make a shadow at all.

Shadows

1. Explain how shadows occur.

____

2. Complete these sentences about shadows:

The nearer the light source to the object, ______________________

The nearer the light source to the screen, ______________________

The larger the object, ______________________

The lower the position of the light source, ______________________

3. List seven ways of changing a shadow. ______________________

____

____

____

____

4. What are the straight lines that show light travelling in a diagram called? ______________________

5. Write one sentence like the ones in question 2 to explain the difference between these two diagrams.

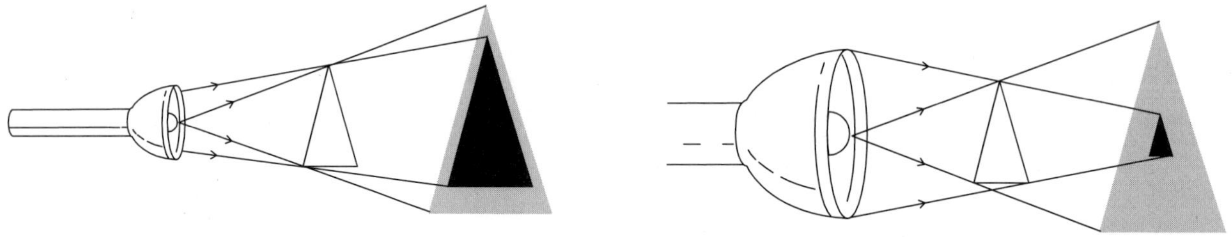

____

Describe a shadow that you have seen outside. How does it change during the day? Explain why this happens.

Shadows

1. What causes a shadow?

____

2. Complete these sentences about shadows:

The nearer the light source to the object, the larger the shadow.

The further the light source from the object,

____

The nearer the light source to the screen,

____

The further the light source from the screen,

____

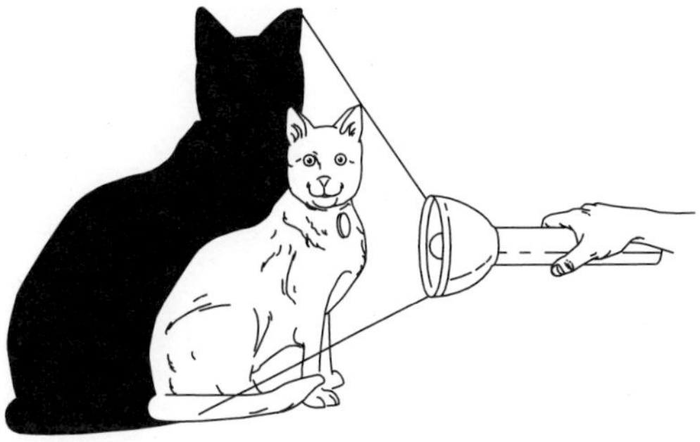

3. List three more things that could be changed to make a difference to the shadow. ______________________________

____

4. What are the straight lines that show light travelling in a diagram called? ______________________________

5. Write one sentence like the ones in question 2 to explain the difference between these two diagrams.

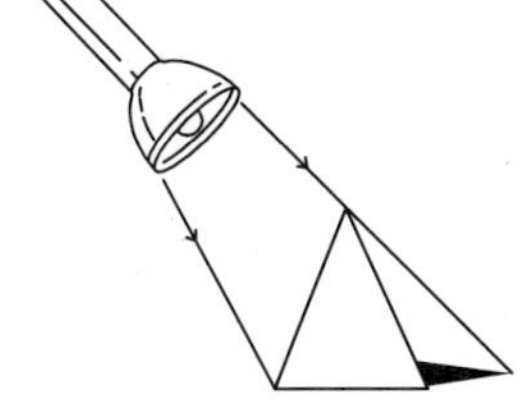

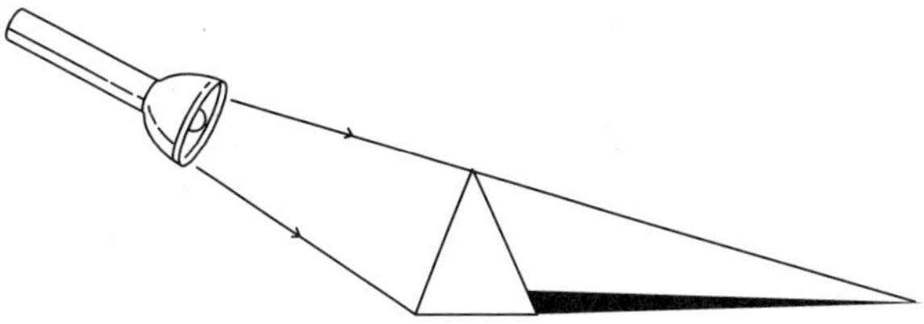

____

Describe a shadow that you have seen outside. How does it change during the day? Explain why this happens.

Shadows drawing game

Teacher instructions

Photocopy these pictures onto thin card and cut them out. Ask the children to sit in pairs, back to back. Give one child in each pair a card and ask them to describe the picture to their partner. The other child should try to draw the picture from the description without looking at the card. Encourage the children to use scientific terms in their descriptions, such as 'shadow', 'light ray', 'Sun' and 'light source'.

Changing shadows

1

A group of pupils designed an investigation to find out how to make a shadow change size. Their instructions have got mixed up.

Put their instructions in order, so that another group can try out their investigation. Your teacher will tell you whether to do this by numbering the instructions, rewriting them or cutting them out and pasting them on another sheet.

Place the object (a tin) 10cm from the torch.
Make a screen from a large piece of card. Clamp it upright.
Repeat until the tin is 90cm from the torch.
Move the tin so it is 20cm from the torch, then measure the shadow again and record its height.
Put a torch on a pile of books.
Put a tape measure on the table stretching from the torch to the screen, a distance of 1 metre.
You will need: some books, a torch, a clamp stand, a large piece of card, a tin, a tape measure, a ruler.
Switch on the torch and measure the height of the shadow made by the tin.
Write down the height of the shadow.

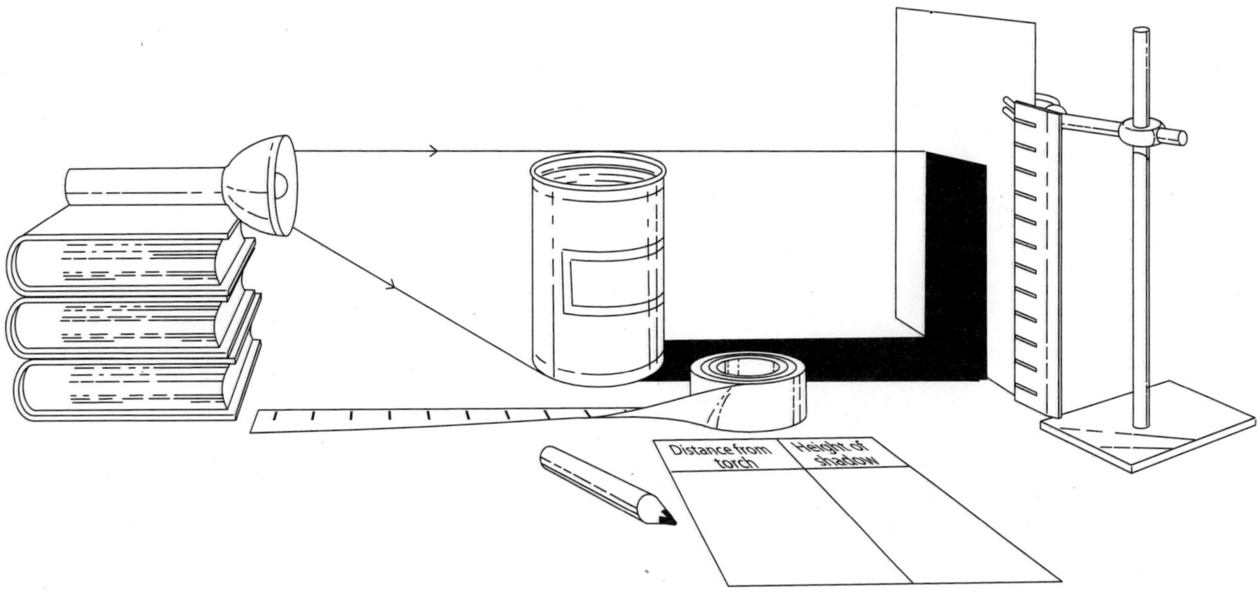

2 Changing shadows

Here are the table and graph drawn by the group of children who were investigating how to make a shadow change size.

Distance from torch (cm)	Height of shadow (cm)
10	39
20	22
30	17
40	16
50	13
60	12.5
70	12
80	11.5
90	11

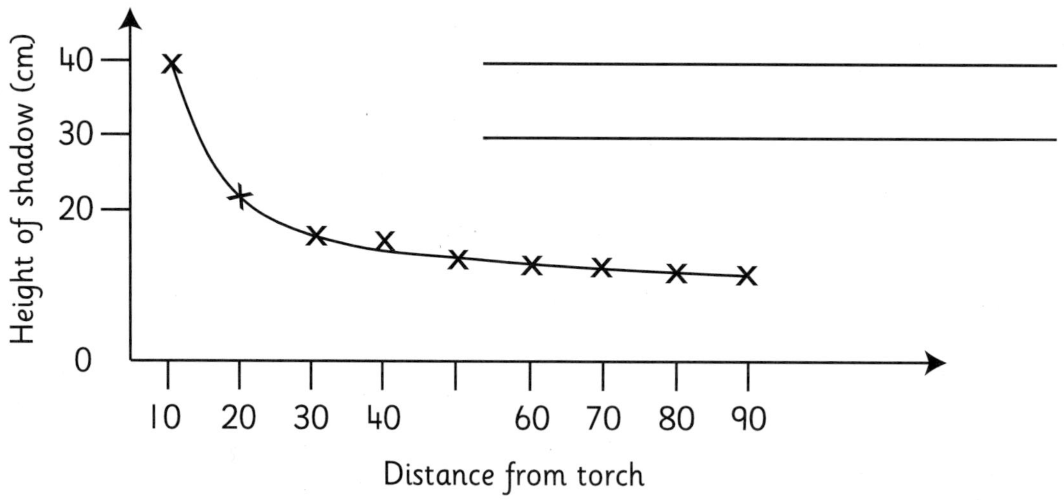

Answer these questions about the table and graph. Write on another sheet of paper or in your book.

1. There are four things missing on the graph. What are they?

2. Complete this sentence. The graph shows that the further the object from the torch…

3. One result does not fit the pattern. What could have gone wrong in the investigation to cause this?

4. Write a list of six questions to go with this graph. Swap questions with a friend. Can you use the graph to answer each other's questions?

Match the mistakes

Here are some graphs drawn by a class of children investigating how to change the size of a shadow. There is something wrong with each graph, and the teacher has written comments on four of them. Which comment matches which graph? Cut out the pairs and stick them together.

Two graphs don't have a teacher comment. Write your own comment for each of these.

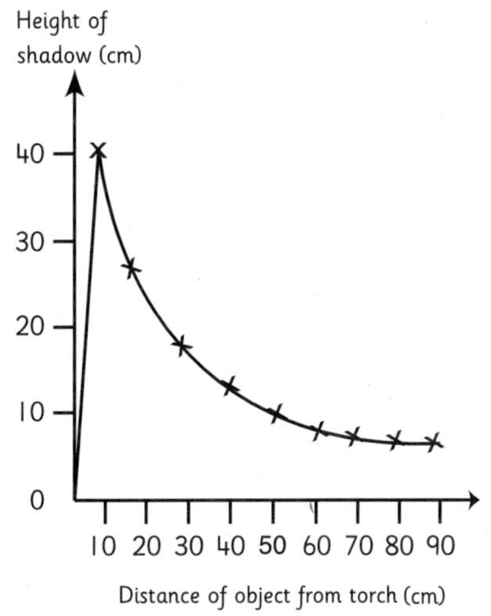

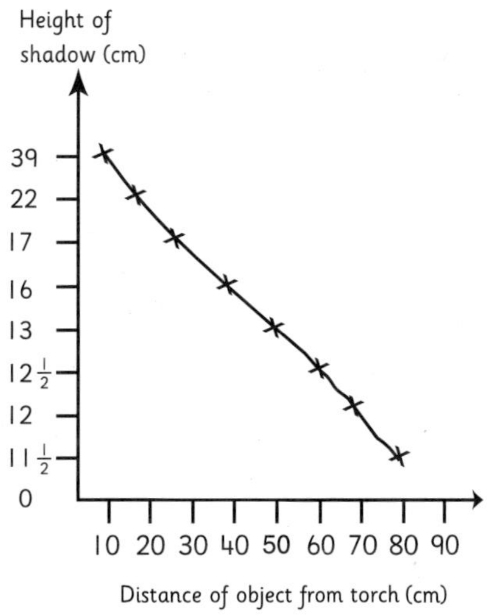

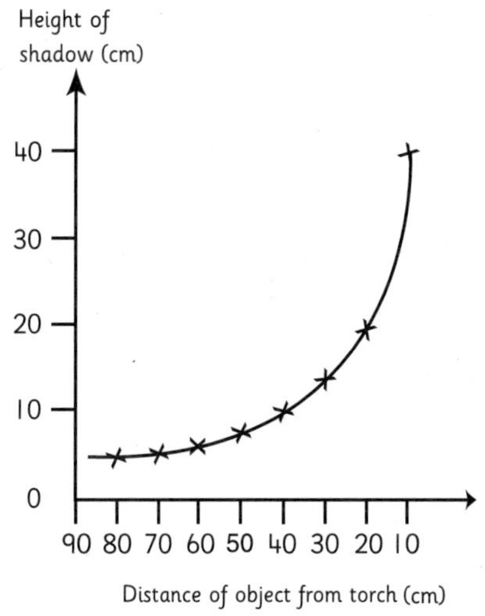

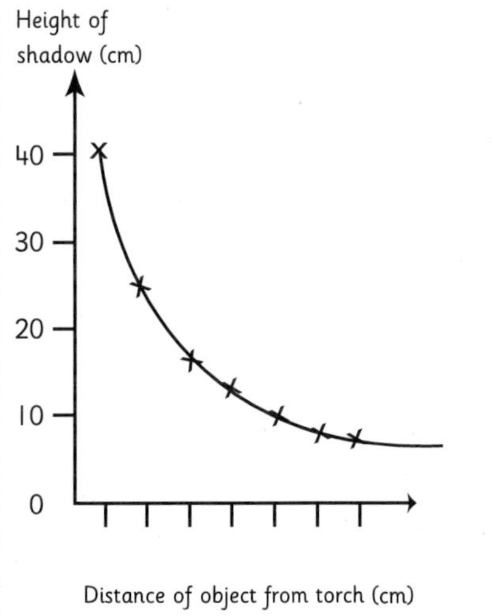

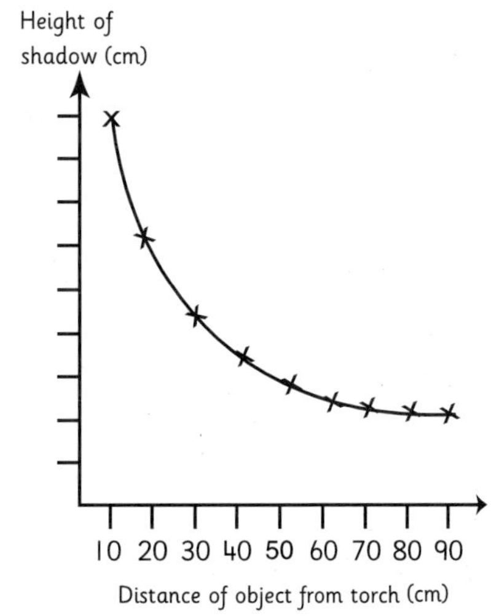

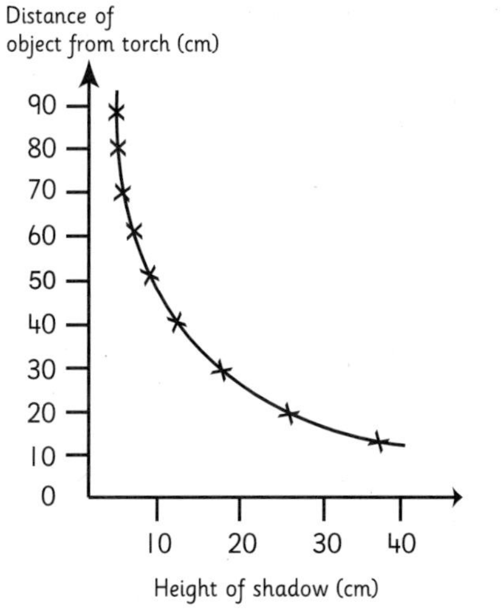

You have not put a scale on the axis showing the height of the shadow.

You have put your <u>results</u> up the side of the graph, not an even <u>scale</u>.

The scale on the axis showing the distance from the torch to the object should be the other way round.

What you <u>changed</u> (distance of object from torch) should go along the bottom, and what you <u>measured</u> (height of shadow) should go up the side.

Shadow puppets

Read this passage through and then write eight sentences about light and shadows. All of the information should be taken from the passage, but you should not copy any sentences directly.

In science lessons, we have been doing some work on shadows. During the topic, our teacher asked us to make shadow puppets and put on a shadow play for some of the younger children in our school. We had to use the things we'd learned about shadows to help us design the puppets.

We had a range of materials to choose from. We chose mostly opaque materials for the puppets, as these materials block the light. We were using a torch as a light source. The light travels in straight lines from the torch and hits the shadow puppets. If the puppets are made from opaque materials, the light cannot pass through and a shadow is formed.

Part of our shadow play was set under the sea. We made fish puppets from card, which blocked the light completely. We made 'wave' shadows from a translucent plastic bag. This material did not block the light completely, so we were able to make fuzzy shadows for the waves. We put some clear blue-green plastic over the torch to make the whole scene appear coloured. The plastic was transparent, so it didn't make a shadow.

Reflection and seeing

Here are some pieces of children's writing about reflection, seeing and how light travels.

Maryam and Shenaz
We can **see light sources** because **light** from them enters our **eyes**. If it is completely **dark**, we cannot see at all. This is because **darkness** is the **absence of light**. Once, on a school trip, we went into some caves. The leader switched off the lights. We could not see anything because there was no light at all.

John, Marion and Anne
We can see **objects** because light is **reflected** from them into our eyes. When we are reading, the light comes from a source such as the Sun or a lamp. The light hits the book and **bounces** into our eyes. This bouncing of light is called **reflection**.

Brenda and Sinéad
Sometimes it would be useful to be able to see around corners. At the end of our road, it is very dangerous because you can't see the cars coming around the corner. You can't see around the corner because **light travels** in **straight lines**. The council have put up a big **mirror** at the end of our road, so we can see the cars coming. We can see them **reflected** in the mirror.

Jeremy and Holly
We made a box to show that **light travels** in **straight lines**. We lined it with black paper, so that light could not be **reflected** inside it. We made three small holes in the box: one in the top and one in each of two opposite sides. If you shine a torch through one of the holes in the side and look through the opposite hole, you can see the light because it is travelling in a straight line to your eye. If you look through the hole in the top, you cannot see the light because it is not travelling to your eye.

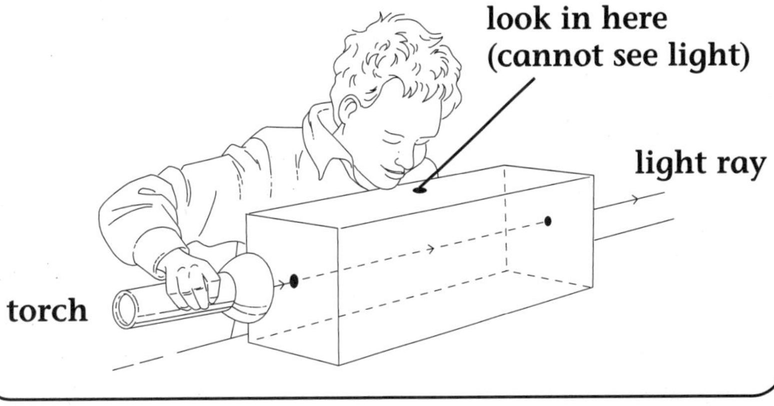

Reflection and seeing

1. Explain the difference between how we see a light source and how we see other objects.

2. What is darkness?

3. Draw and label a diagram to show why the council put up a mirror at the end of Brenda and Sinéad's road.

4. Explain how Jeremy and Holly's box shows that light travels in straight lines.

5. What are the three most important facts that the pupils' pieces of writing tell us about light? Write in sentences.

Imagine you live across the road from your friend. How could you send your friend a message at night using a torch? Write about sending the message. What equipment would you need? How would you use it? What problems might you have?

Reflection and seeing

1. Look at Maryam and Shenaz's piece of writing. Explain how we see.

____

____

2. Explain why the children could not see inside the caves when the lights were switched off. ______________________________

3. What is reflection? ______________________________

____

4. Why did the council put up a mirror at the end of Brenda and Sinéad's road? ______________________________

____

5. Why couldn't cars be seen around the corner without the mirror?

____

6. How does Jeremy and Holly's box show that light travels in straight lines? ______________________________

____

7. What are the three most important facts that the pupils' pieces of writing tell us about light? Write in sentences.

____

____

____

____

Imagine you live across the road from your friend. How could you send your friend a message at night using a torch? Write about sending the message. What equipment would you need? How would you use it? What problems might you have?

How we see

Draw light rays on these diagrams. Next to each diagram, write an explanation of how the light source or object can be seen.

The book can be seen

I can see the tree

The stars

but the Moon

The driver can see

Up periscope!

This series of six diagrams shows how to make and use a cardboard periscope. Under diagrams 1 to 5, write instructions to help someone make and use the periscope. Under diagram 6, explain how the periscope works.

1

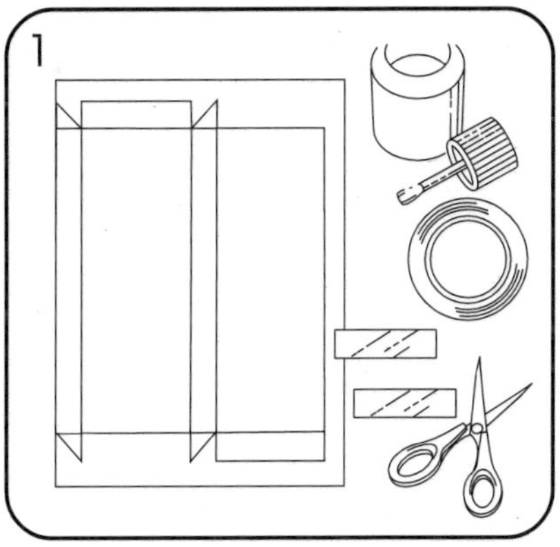

2

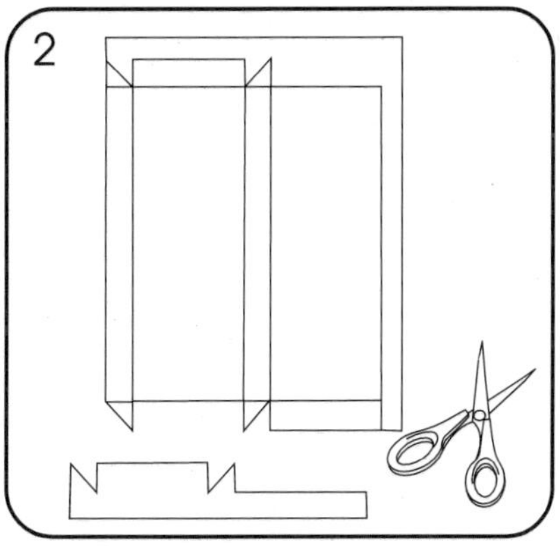

3

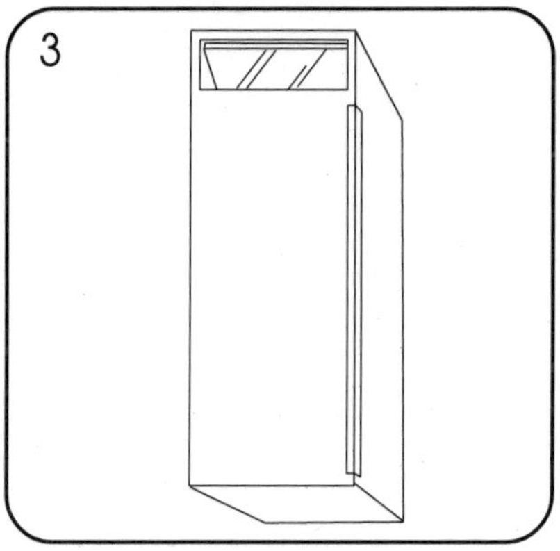

4

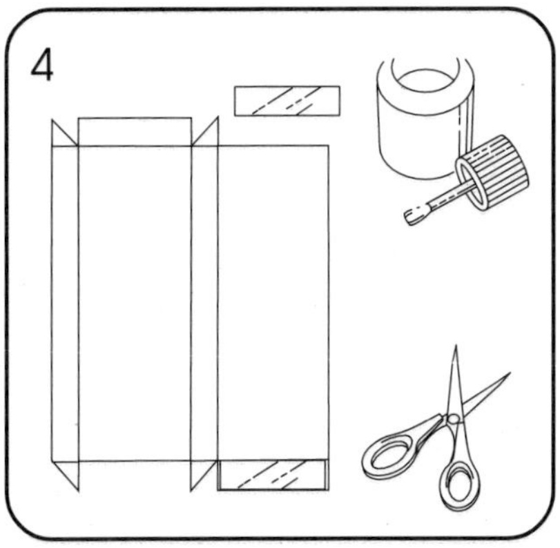

5

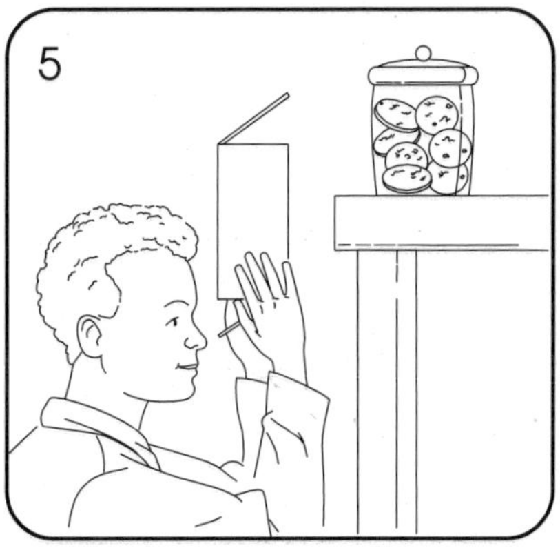

6

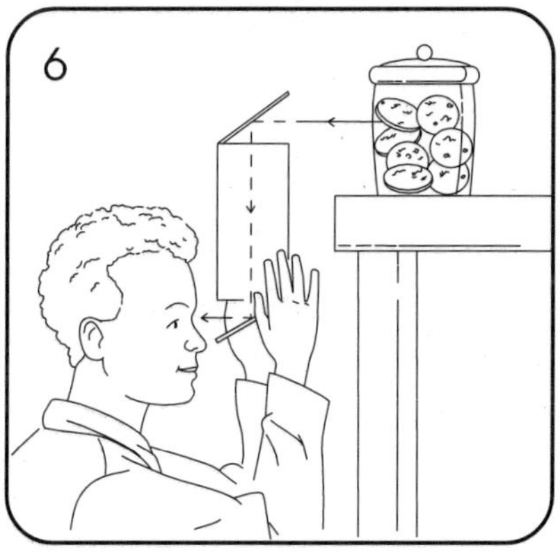

Seeing things?

Look at the pictures and the pupils' explanations. Write responses to these pupils, explaining why their statements are incorrect.

I can see you in the dark because I eat a lot of carrots.
I can see myself in the mirror because the light shines out of my eyes to the mirror and back again.

My diagram shows how the light travels so I can see the biscuits on the table through the periscope.

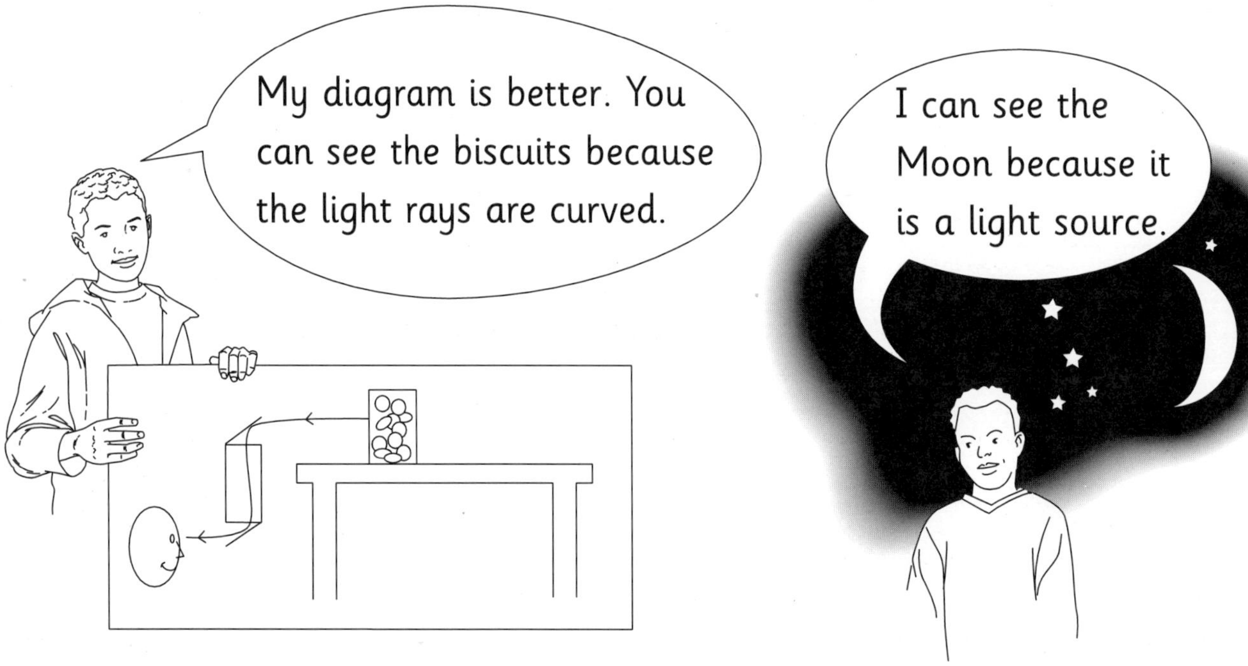
My diagram is better. You can see the biscuits because the light rays are curved.
I can see the Moon because it is a light source.

Reflection and seeing bingo

1

Teacher instructions

You need: This sheet of questions, a bag or box, bingo cards from page 66.

What to do: Cut out the question cards and put them into the bag or box. Share out the bingo cards between the children. Pull one question out at a time and read it aloud, or ask a child to do this. The children tick off the answer on their cards. When they have completed a horizontal line, they can call out 'Bingo!'

Light travels in...	We can see because light enters our...	The absence of light is called...
We see objects because they...	Something that gives out light is called a...	The bouncing of light is called...
Light cannot travel...	To see around a corner, you could use a...	A periscope helps you see around corners because it has...
One thing that is not a light source, but reflects light from the Sun, is...	To make a periscope, you need...	You cannot see anything at all if it is completely...

2

Reflection and seeing bingo

straight lines	eyes	darkness	reflect light
light source	reflection	around corners	periscope
mirrors inside	the Moon	two mirrors	dark

eyes	darkness	reflect light	light source
reflection	around corners	periscope	mirrors inside
the Moon	two mirrors	dark	straight lines

darkness	reflect light	light source	reflection
around corners	periscope	mirrors inside	the Moon
two mirrors	dark	straight lines	eyes

reflect light	light source	reflection	around corners
periscope	mirrors inside	the Moon	two mirrors
dark	straight lines	eyes	darkness

reflect light	mirrors inside	eyes	around corners
light source	the Moon	darkness	periscope
straight lines	reflection	two mirrors	dark

mirrors inside	eyes	around corners	light source
the Moon	darkness	periscope	straight lines
reflection	two mirrors	dark	reflect light

eyes	around corners	light source	the Moon
darkness	periscope	straight lines	reflection
two mirrors	dark	reflect light	mirrors inside

Our Solar System

A group of **planets** circling around a **star** is called a **solar system**. Our **Sun** is a star. It is a ball of hot **gases** which, although it is 150 million kilometres (93 million miles) away, is our main **source** of **heat** and **light**.

Earth is one of the nine planets that travel around the Sun. The others are **Mercury**, **Venus**, **Mars**, **Jupiter**, **Saturn**, **Uranus**, **Neptune** and **Pluto**. Mercury is the nearest planet to the Sun. Earth is the third planet from the Sun.

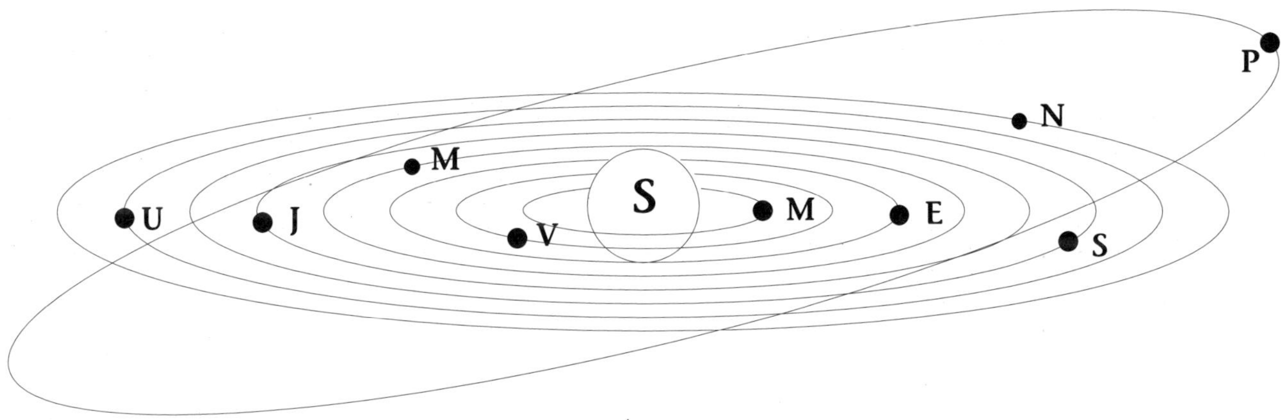

Each planet travels around the Sun in an almost circular **orbit**. Most of the time Pluto is the planet furthest from the Sun, but occasionally Neptune is the furthest away because Pluto's orbit is slightly tilted. Uranus, Pluto and Neptune are extremely cold because they are so far from the Sun. Mercury is very hot because it is so close to the Sun. However, the hottest planet is Venus. It has an **atmosphere** that traps heat, whereas Mercury has no atmosphere. An atmosphere is a layer of gases surrounding a planet.

As far as we know, Earth is the only planet where animals and plants can live. This is because Earth has water on the surface, an atmosphere that animals can breathe and plants can use to help them grow, and the right **temperature** for living things. We need all these things, as well as light from the Sun, for survival.

Our Solar System

1. What is a solar system? ____________________

2. Why do we need the Sun? ____________________

3. List the nine planets in order, starting with the one closest to the Sun.

4. Why is Venus hotter than Mercury?

5. Which planet would you predict to be the coldest and why?

6. Which planet is occasionally the furthest from the Sun? ____________

Draw a simple diagram on another sheet to explain why.

7. What conditions on Earth make it possible for living things to survive there? ____________________

Choose a planet (not the Earth), and write a factfile about it. Include facts such as its distance from the Sun, its temperature, the length of a day and a year on that planet, and whether it has any moons. You will need to use information sources such as reference books, CD-ROMs or Internet sites.

Our Solar System

1. What is a solar system? ______________________________

____

2. What is our star called? ______________________________

3. Why do we need the Sun? ______________________________

____

4. List the nine planets in order, starting with the one closest to the Sun.

____

____

5. Which planet is furthest from the Sun most of the time?

____

6. Which is the hottest planet? ______________________________

7. Which planet would you predict to be the coldest? Why did you choose this planet? ______________________________

____

8. What makes Earth a good planet for animals and plants to live on?

____

____

____

____

Choose a planet (not the Earth), and write a factfile about it. Include facts such as its distance from the Sun, its temperature, the length of a day and a year on that planet, and whether it has any moons. You will need to use information sources such as reference books, CD-ROMs or Internet sites.

Planets database

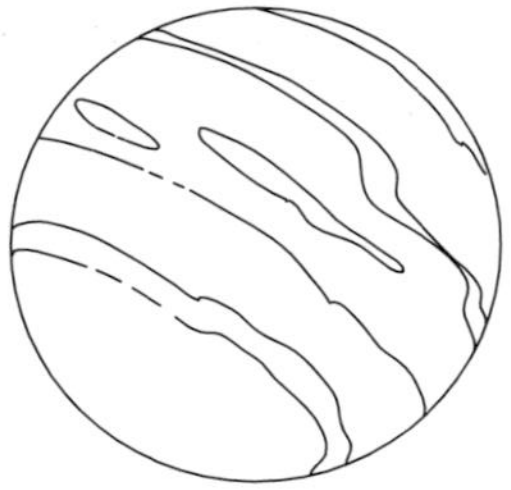

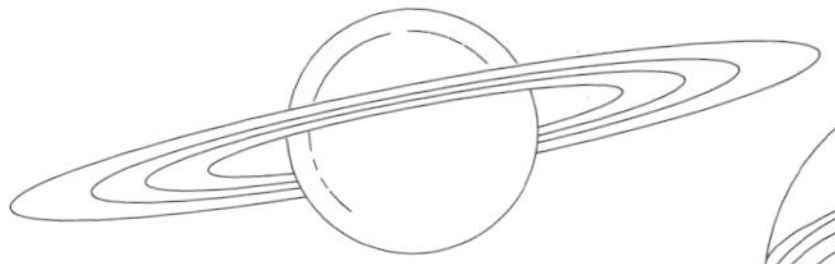
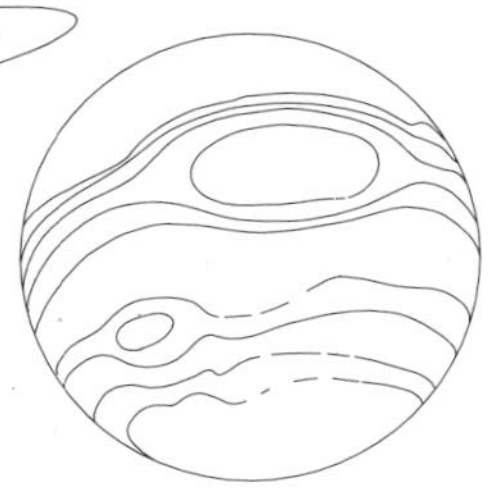

This table of information about the planets has some sections missing. By reading the information, try to predict what should be in the empty sections and add the missing information to the table.

	Average distance from Sun in million km (and million miles)				Number of moons	
Mercury	58 (36)	100°C	88 Earth days	59 Earth days	0	none
Venus	108 (67)	460°C	225 Earth days	243 Earth days	0	carbon dioxide
Earth	150 (93)	22°C	365¼ Earth days	24 Earth hours	1	mostly nitrogen and oxygen
	229 (142)	–23°C	687 Earth days	24.6 Earth hours	2	carbon dioxide
Jupiter		–150°C	12 Earth years	9.8 Earth hours	more than 20	ammonia and methane
Saturn	1426 (886)	–180°C	29½ Earth years	10.2 Earth hours	more than 20	hydrogen and helium
Uranus	2871 (1783)	–210°C		17.9 Earth hours	5	methane and hydrogen
Neptune	4498 (2794)		165 Earth years	19.2 Earth hours	8	methane and hydrogen
	5909 (3670)		249 Earth years	6.4 Earth days	1	none

Finding out about the planets

You need: Scissors, a pen, your completed 'Planets database' sheet.

Look at the 'Planets database' sheet and use it to help you complete these quiz cards. Then cut out the quiz cards and give them to another group in your class, so they can try to match the questions and answers.

Planets with more than 20 moons	
Hottest planet	
Coldest planet	
Planet nearest to the Sun	
Planets with one moon	
Planet with the longest day	
Planet with the shortest year	
Planets with no atmosphere	
Planet with the shortest day	
Planet with the longest year	
Planet with oxygen in its atmosphere	
Planet 150 million kilometres from the Sun	

Making a booklet

You need: the 'Planet travel guide' sheet from page 73 (enlarged to A3) and reference materials about the planets **or** the 'Space dictionary' sheet from page 80 (enlarged to A3); scissors.

What to do

1. Fold the sheet in half.

2. Fold it in half again.

3. Fold it in half again.

4. Open it out and fold it like this:

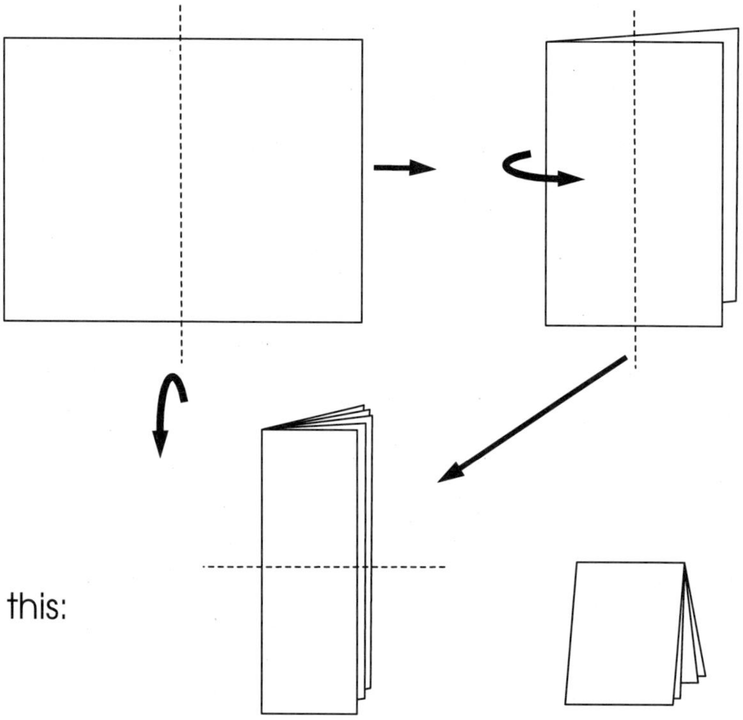

5. Cut from the fold to the bottom.

6. Open the sheet like this:

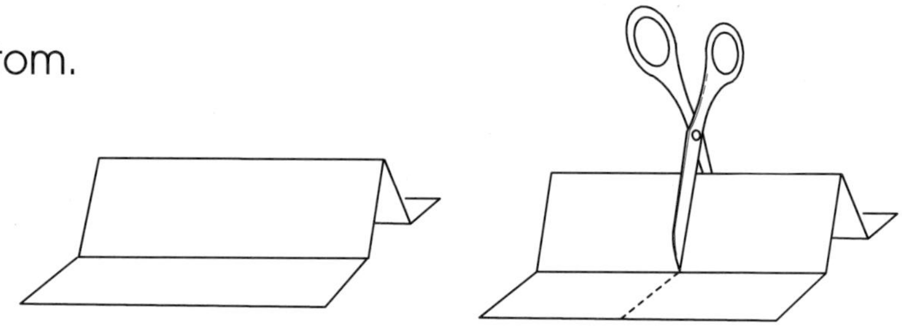

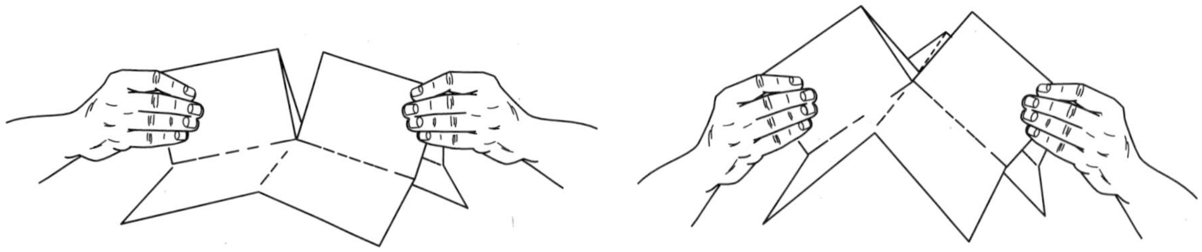

7. Fold it up so the title is on the front.

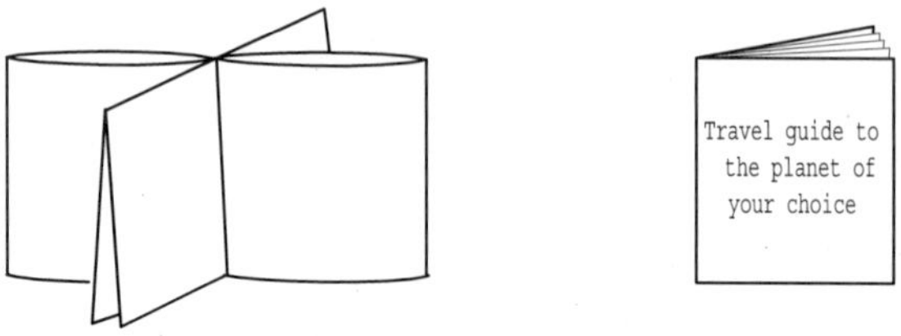

8. Complete the 'Planet travel guide' by adding information from reference books, CD-ROMs or Internet sites. You will need to use your imagination too! **or** Write in the 'Space dictionary' what each word means. You can add pictures if you have room.

Planet travel guide

How to get there	Travel guide to the planet of your choice Planet: ________ Author: ________
Weather conditions	Prices
Landscape	Accommodation
Tourist attractions	What to take with you

Enlarge to A3 size

Remembering the planets

This is one way to remember the order of the planets in the solar system:

My	Very	Easy	Method	Just	Speeds	Up	Naming	Planets
Mercury	Venus	Earth	Mars	Jupiter	Saturn	Uranus	Neptune	Pluto

Try to make up another memory aid (called a 'mnemonic') to help you remember the order of the planets. You can list them in reverse order (starting with Pluto) if you prefer.

______ ______ ______ ______ ______ ______ ______ ______ ______

Sometimes it's easier to remember the meaning or spelling of a word if it is illustrated in a way that helps you to visualise it. For example:

Try to illustrate these words and phrases to help you remember them.

atmosphere   solar system   Saturn   Pluto   Earth

Time and space

What is a **year**? What is a **day**? What is a **month**? We can begin to answer some of these questions by observing the **Sun**, **Earth** and **Moon**.

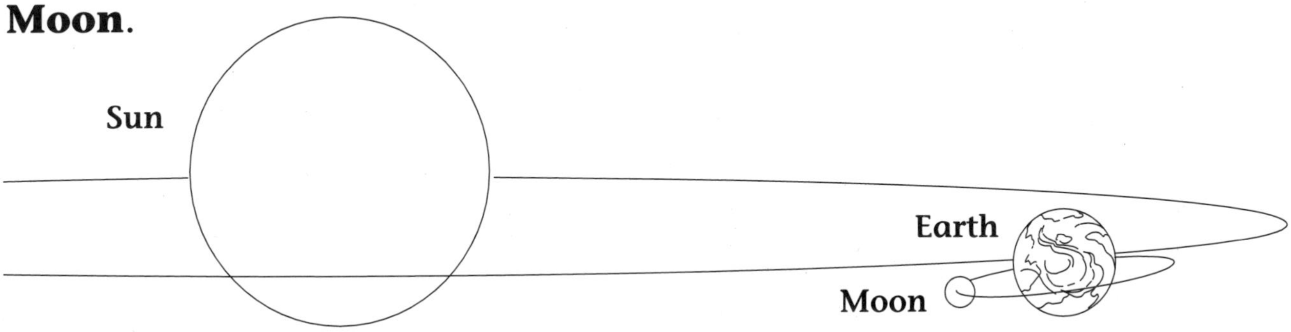

In our **solar system**, there are nine **planets** travelling around the **Sun**. The planets travel in roughly circular paths called **orbits**. The time taken for a planet to complete a full orbit is its **year**. The years are shortest for the planets closest to the Sun.

Each planet also spins around or **rotates** on its **axis** (an imaginary line through the centre of the planet). The time it takes for a planet to rotate once is known as its **day**. Daytime and **night** occur because of this **rotation**. At any one time, half of the planet will be facing away from the Sun. It is **night** on this half.

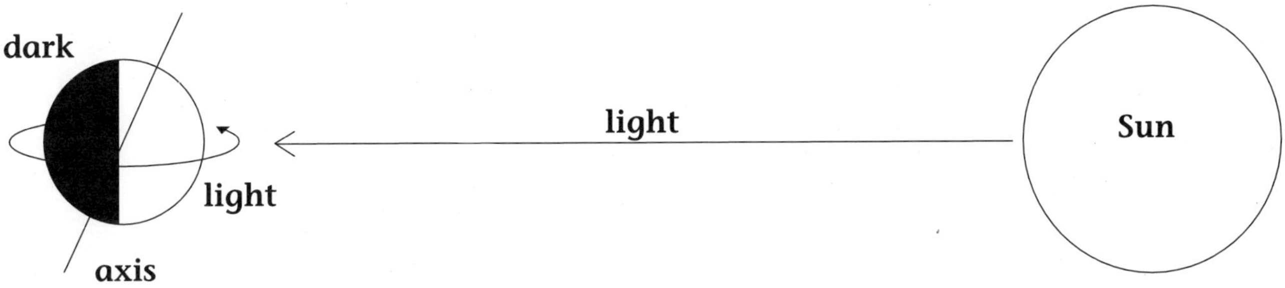

Some planets, such as Earth, rotate quite quickly. Others rotate much more slowly – on Venus, a day is about 240 times longer than on Earth.

Some planets have **satellites** travelling around them, called **moons**. Our Moon takes roughly one **month** to orbit the Earth. The Moon appears to change shape because we cannot see the whole of its lit side all the time. The different shapes we see over a **lunar month** are called the **phases of the Moon**.

Time and space

1. Explain the terms **year** and **day**.

____

____

____

____

____

____

2. What causes night?______________________________

____

____

3. How long is a complete day on Earth (in hours)?__________

4. About how long is a day on Venus?__________________

5. What is the scientific name for a moon?_______________

6. How long does our Moon's orbit take?_______________

7. What do we call the pattern of different shapes of the Moon that we see?____________________

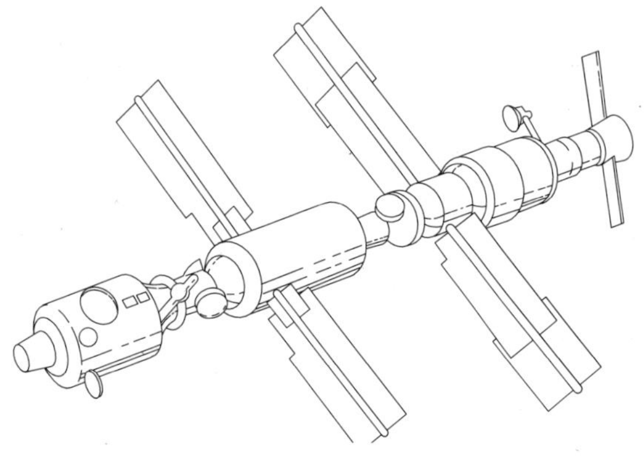

Moons are sometimes called **natural** satellites. Find out what **artificial satellites** are. What are they used for? Use books about space exploration, or Internet sites such as the NASA site, to find out more about one artificial satellite.

Time and space

1. What is a year?____

____

____

2. What is a day?____

____

____

3. Why is it dark at night?________________________________

____

4. How long is a complete day on Earth (in hours)?________________

5. About how long is a day on Venus?________________

6. What is the scientific name for a moon?________________

7. How long does it take our Moon to orbit the Earth?________________

8. What do we call the pattern of different shapes of the Moon that we see? ________________

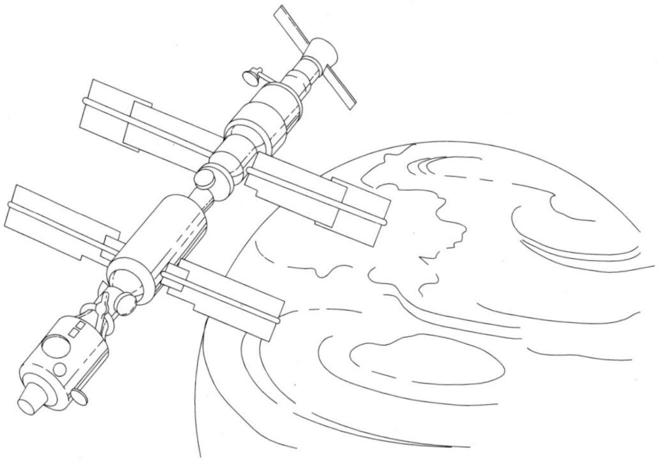

Moons are sometimes called **natural** satellites. Find out what **artificial satellites** are. What are they used for? Use books about space exploration, or Internet sites such as the NASA site, to find out more about one artificial satellite.

1 The phases of the Moon

Follow the instructions to make a booklet about the way the shape of the Moon appears to change.

1. Make a square of paper by making a diagonal fold in an A4 sheet and cutting off the part that sticks out.

2. Open out the square and fold it in half diagonally the other way.

(a)

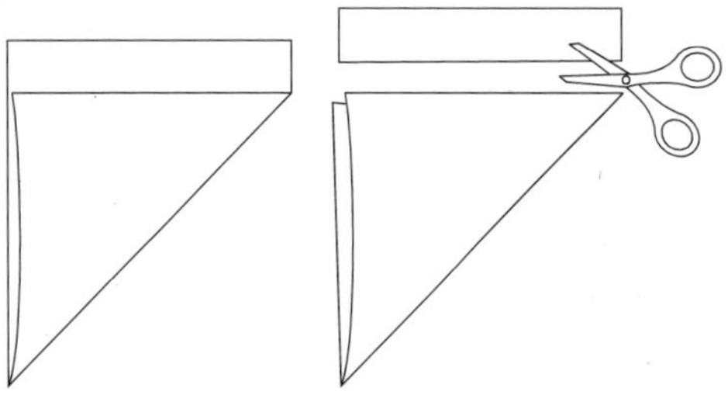

(b)

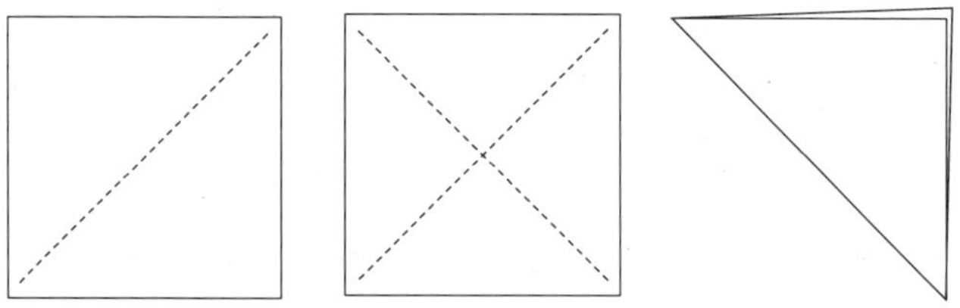

3. Open it out again and fold each corner into the centre.

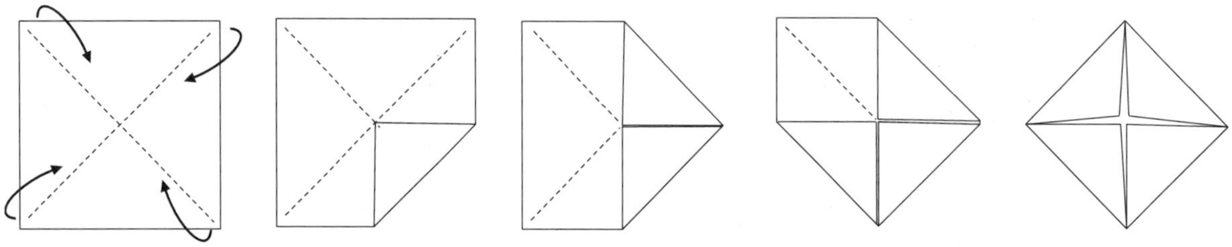

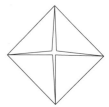

4. Now cut each flap in half along the fold, so the booklet has eight flaps.

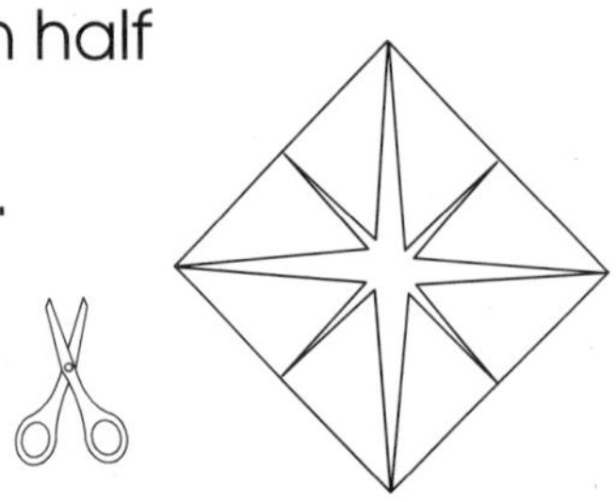

Did you know?
Waxing means growing.
Waning means shrinking.

5. On each flap, draw one of these shapes of the Moon. Keep the shapes in this order.

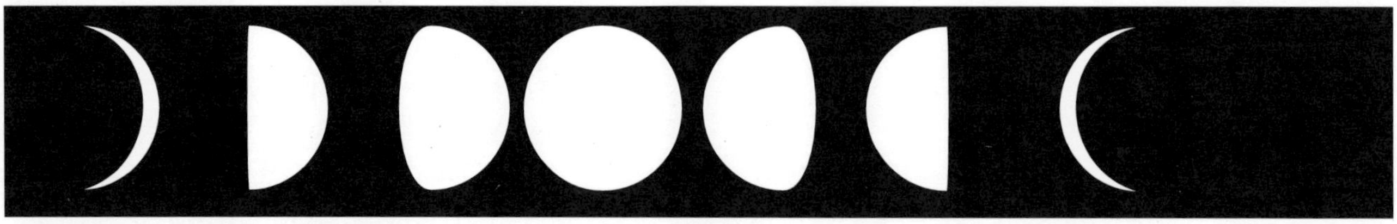

crescent Moon (waxing)	**half Moon (waxing)**	**gibbous Moon (waxing)**	**full Moon**	**gibbous Moon (waning)**	**half Moon (waning)**	**crescent Moon (waning)**	**new Moon (not visible)**

6. Inside each flap, write the date when the Moon appears to be this shape. If it's too cloudy for you to observe this yourself, check in the newspaper. A waxing Moon is visible in the evening, a full Moon is visible all night, and a waning Moon is visible in the early morning.

The phases of the Moon

2

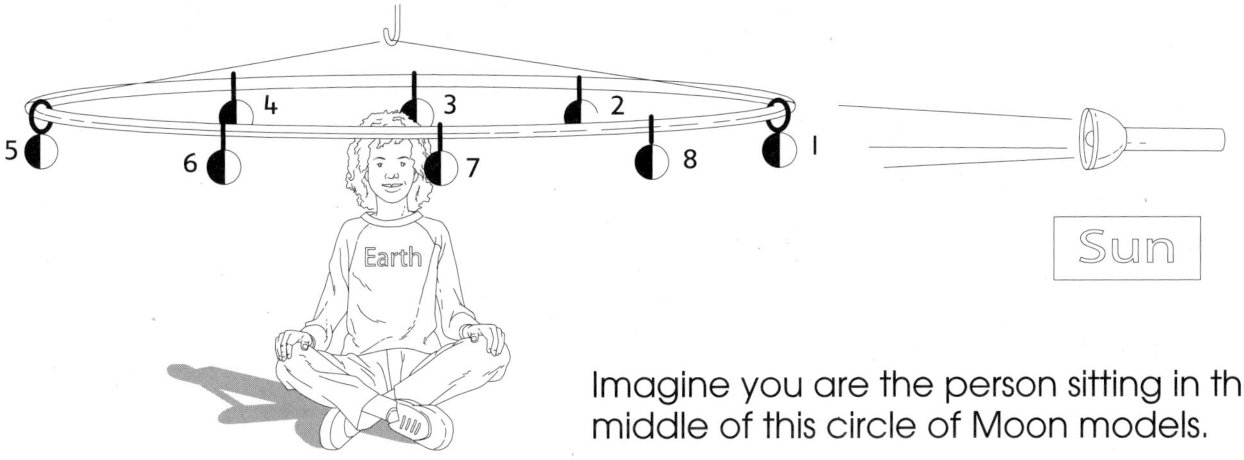

Imagine you are the person sitting in the middle of this circle of Moon models.

Write numbers to match the labels to the Moon positions. Add writing to the labels that only have pictures.

____
____
____

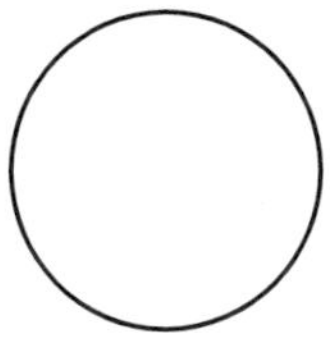

Now I can see half of the lit side of the Moon. It appears to be still growing (waxing).

____
____
____

I can hardly see any of the lit side of the Moon at all. It is a new Moon.

This one is about a quarter size. It is still fairly new.

The Moon appears to be getting smaller (waning) now, but I can still see about three quarters of it.

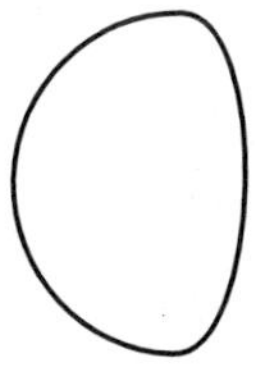

____
____
____

I can see about three quarters of the Moon now, but it is not yet full.

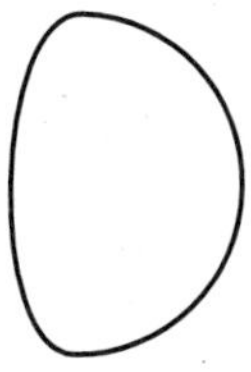

Space and time dictionary

Follow the instructions on page 72, 'Making a booklet'. Enlarge to A3 size

Space and time dictionary

Name: ____________

atmosphere

day

Earth

month

Sun

year

Moon

orbit

solar system

star

phases of the Moon

planet

rotation

satellite

Energy sources

All these **devices** need **energy** to make them work. They use a **battery** as an **energy source**.

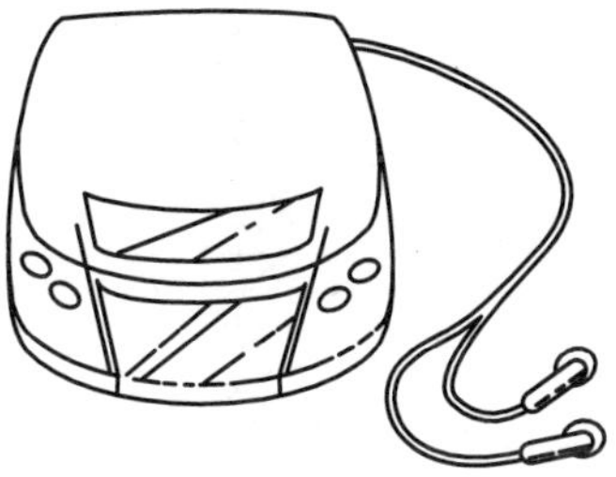

personal stereo

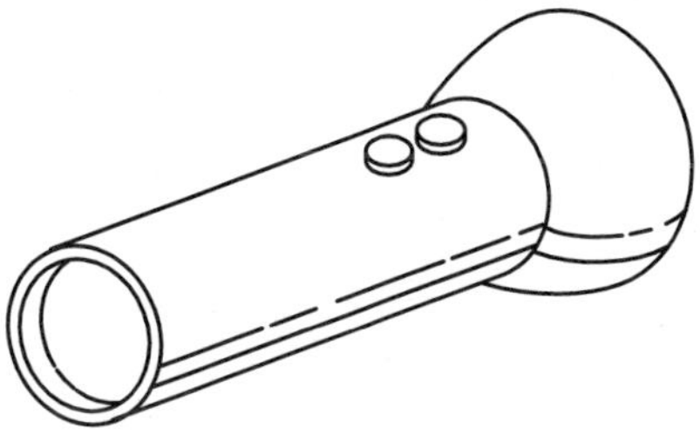

torch

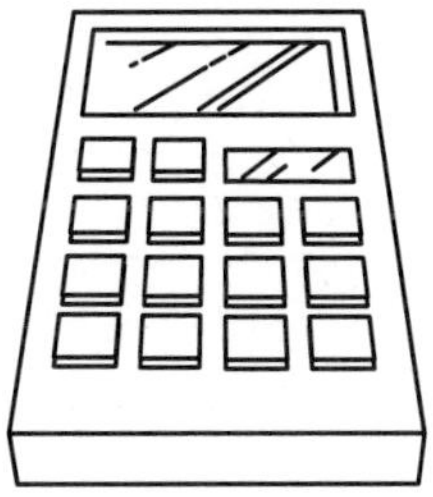

calculator

The battery inside each device **stores** the energy. When the device is switched on, the battery **supplies electrical energy**. The personal stereo can be plugged into the **mains** instead. Then the electrical energy does not come from a battery, but is **generated** in a **power station** and **supplied** to our homes through wires. Many power stations burn a **fuel** (a **store** of energy) such as **coal** to **release heat energy** that can be changed into electrical energy.

Some calculators don't have a battery, but contain a little **solar cell** that changes **light energy** into the electrical energy needed to make the calculator work. Some children's toys use energy from the wind or water to make them work.

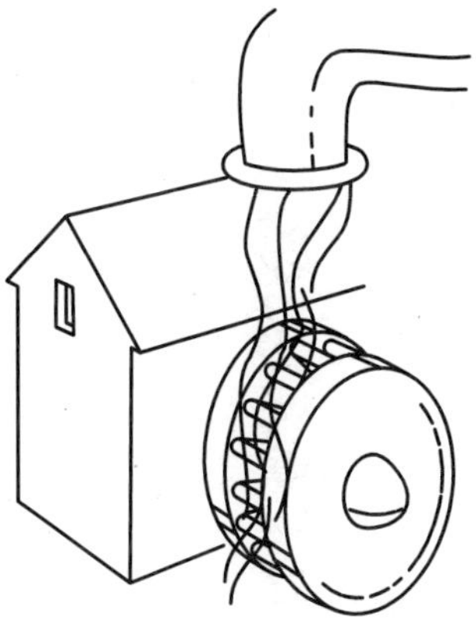

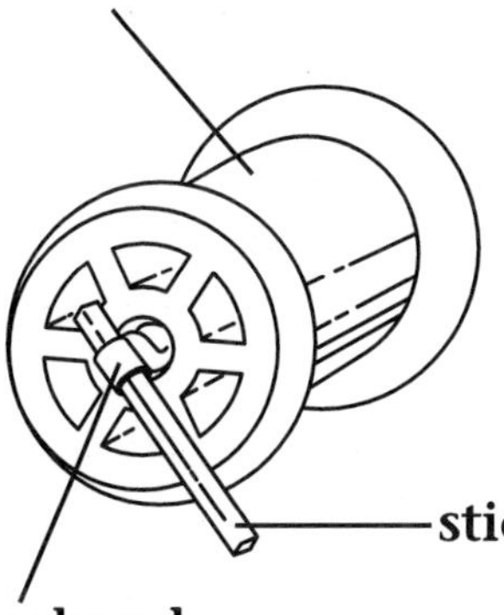

Energy can be **stored** in toys too. The cotton reel crawler shown above works by using energy stored in a twisted rubber band.

Energy is stored in **food** too. We eat food in order to obtain the energy we need to make our bodies work.

Energy sources

1. Give two examples of a source of electrical energy.

2. Where is mains electricity generated, and how does it reach our homes?

3. What type of energy does a solar-powered calculator use?

4. Give two other natural energy sources.

5. Give two examples of energy being stored.

6. What is the energy source of your body?

7. What energy sources can be used to heat homes and schools?

8. Give three examples of devices that work because of stored energy in a rubber band or spring.

In a group, design a table to find out what energy sources the people in your class use to heat their homes. Collect the information from your class.

Energy sources

1. List three things that need a battery to supply the energy that makes them work. ______________________ ______________________

____

2. What kind of energy does the battery provide? ______________________

3. What is mains electricity? ______________________

____

4. Where is mains electricity generated? ______________________

____

5. What energy source for power stations does the text mention?

____

6. What type of energy does a solar-powered calculator use?

____

7. Name two other energy sources used to make toys work.

______________________ ______________________

8. Give two examples of energy being stored.

____

____

9. What is the energy source for your body? ______________________

10. What energy sources might be used to heat homes and schools?

____

____

In a group, design a table to find out what energy sources the people in your class use to heat their homes. Collect the information from your class.

Heating our homes

This graph was produced by a group of pupils to show the energy sources used in their homes for heating.

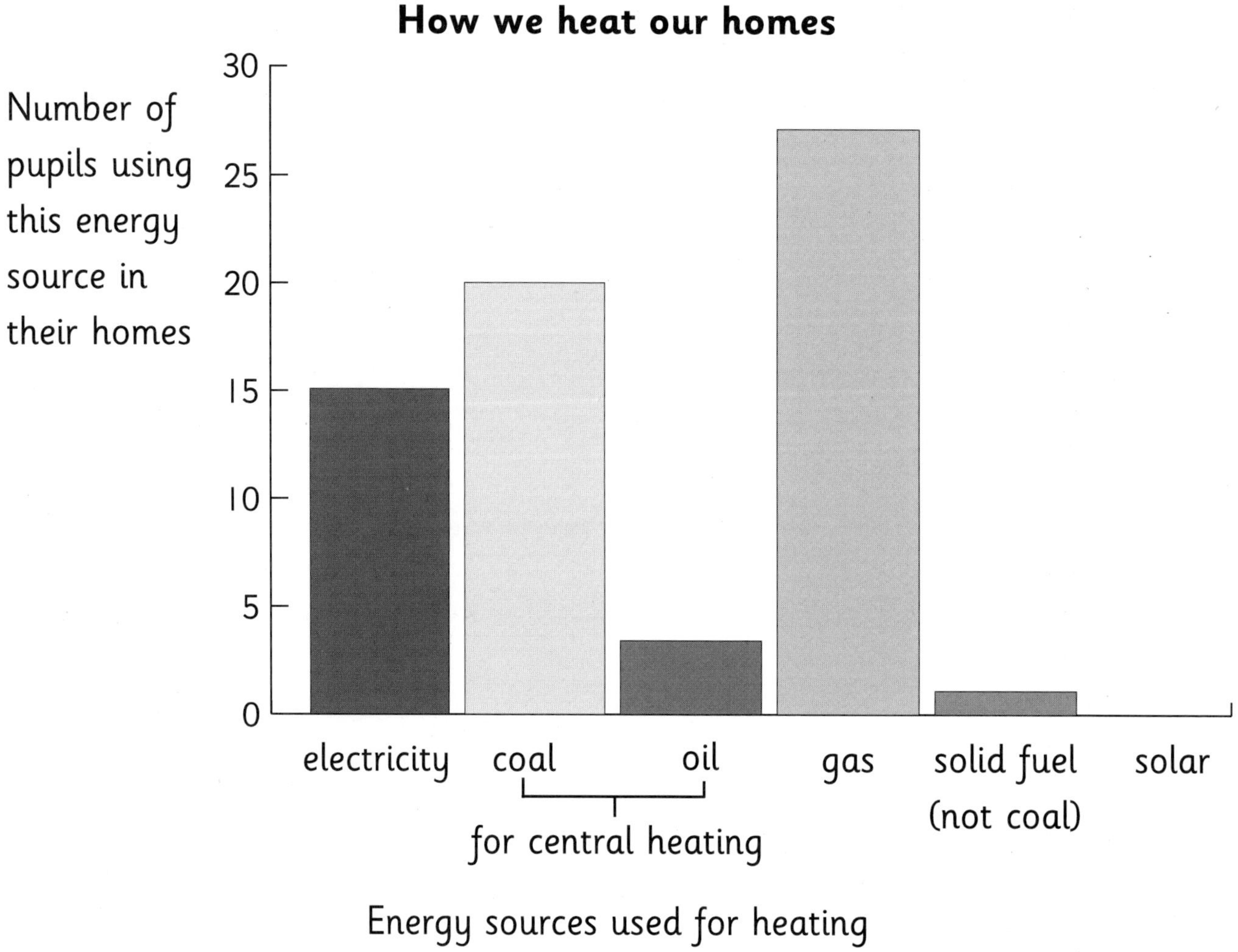

Answer these questions about the graph.

1. Altogether, how many different energy sources were used in the pupils' homes?________________________________

2. Which was the less popular of the fuels used for central heating?

____

3. How many pupils have electrical heating in their homes?

____

Now write some questions of your own about the graph. Ask a friend to read and answer your questions.

Energy sources table

Draw a table to show what energy sources are used by each of these things.

television

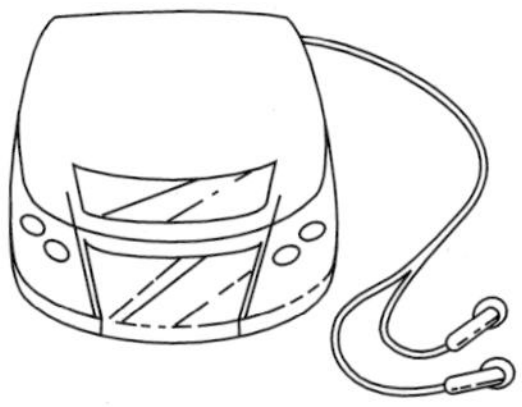
personal stereo

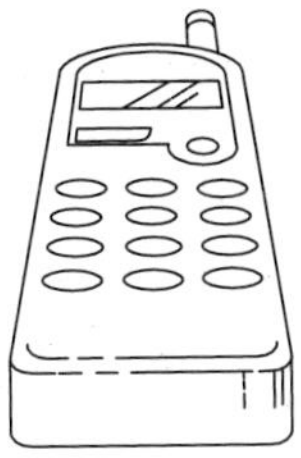
mobile telephone

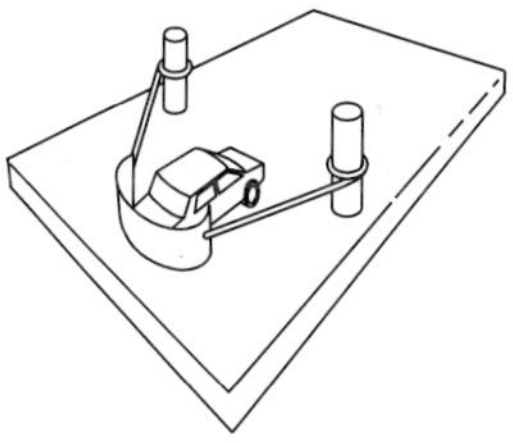
catapult

Jack-in-the-box

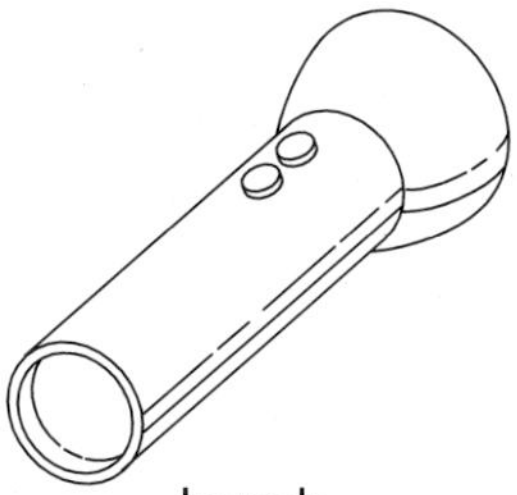
torch

calculator

toy windmill

car

human

rubber band crawler

table lamp

kettle

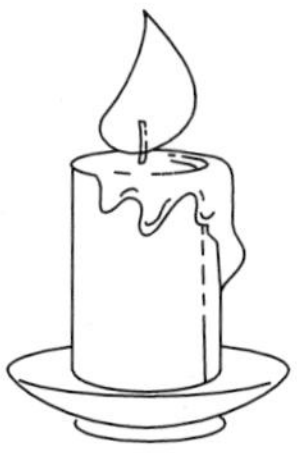
candle

dog

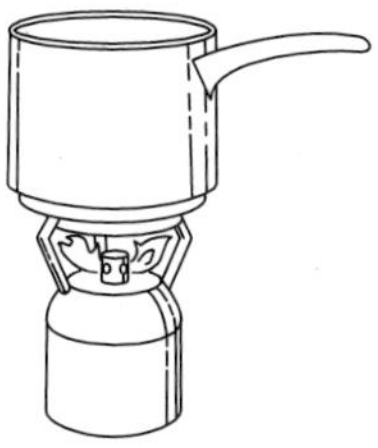
camping stove

wind-up toy

steam train

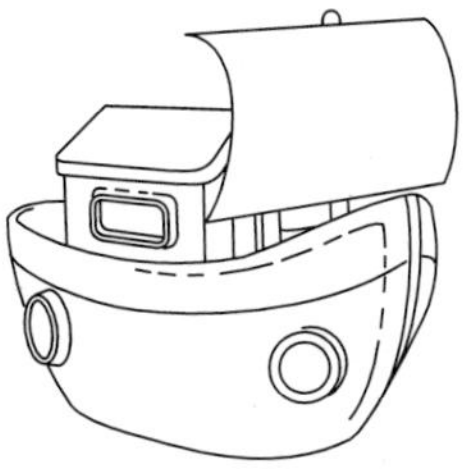
toy boat

windmill

Solar-powered oven

This group of pupils have made and tested a model solar-powered oven. Rewrite their report in the form of instructions, so that members of your class could carry out the same investigation.

Simon, Delyth and Debs

We were investigating how to make a solar-powered oven.

Apparatus: a polystyrene cup, a black plastic bin liner, cling film, card, aluminium foil, a tin of baked beans, a thermometer, a tin opener, sticky tape, scissors.

What we did: First of all, we cut a piece of black plastic from a clean bin liner and used it to line the cup. We half-filled the cup with baked beans, measured the temperature of the beans and covered the cup with cling film.

Next, we covered a large piece of card with foil to reflect light. We made the card into a cone shape around the cup. The foil was inside the cone to reflect light from the Sun into the cup.

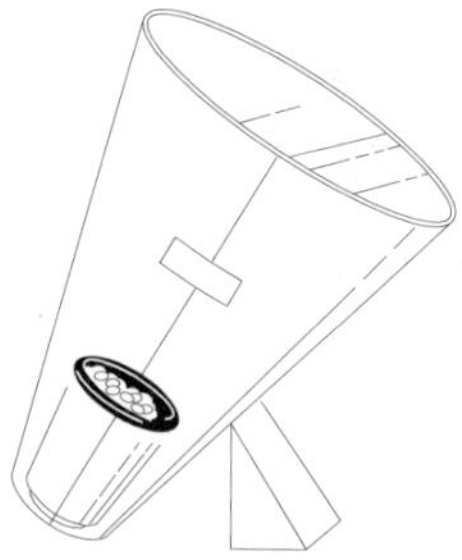

We propped up our oven outside, pointing at the Sun, and left it for half an hour. Then we tested the temperature of the beans.

What we observed: The original temperature of the beans was 22°C. After half an hour in the oven, they had reached 51°C. They were quite warm.

What had happened: The light from the Sun had been reflected into the cup and had caused the beans to heat up.

Making vehicles

These instructions for making and using a vehicle have become mixed up. Put them in the correct order. Ask your teacher whether to cut and paste the instructions or rewrite them.

A

Put the crawler on the floor and let it go. Measure how far it goes.

Hold one end of the rubber band in place with a matchstick.

Twist the pencil around to store energy in the wound-up rubber band.

Thread a rubber band through the centre of a cotton reel.

Fasten the matchstick in place with sticky tape.

Only one end of the pencil should stick out beyond the cotton reel.

Thread a pencil through the other end of the rubber band.

Change the number of twists in the rubber band and test to find out whether this makes a difference to the distance travelled by the vehicle.

The instructions for making this vehicle are lost altogether, but the pictures are in the correct order. Write an instruction to go with each picture.

B

1

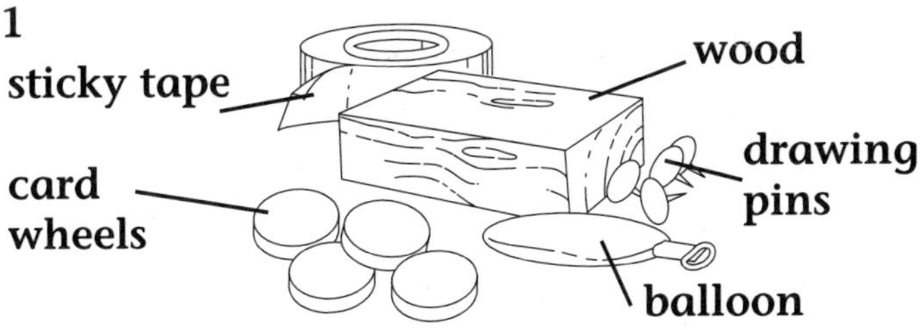

2

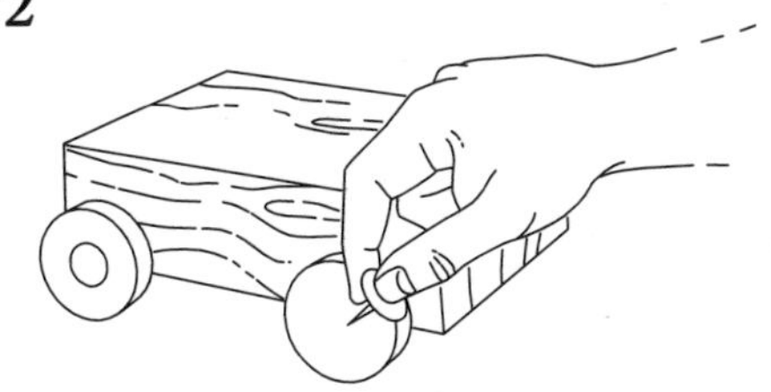

3

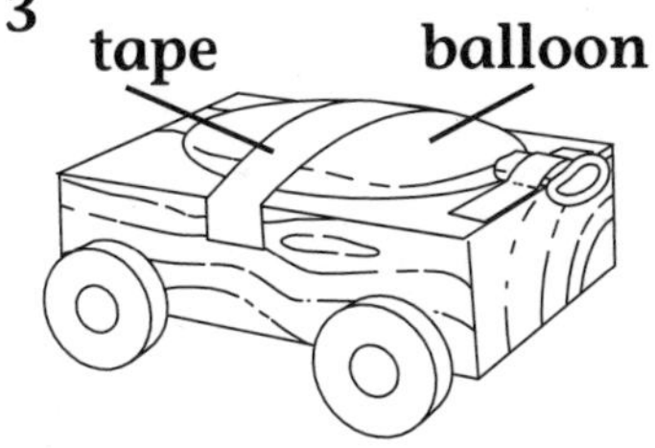

4

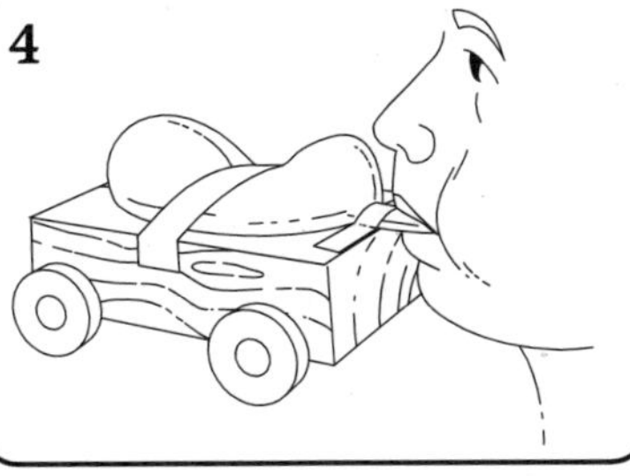

5

Energy sources card game

Teacher instructions
Photocopy onto card. Cut along the dotted lines. Fold each card along the solid line, with the text on the outside, and fasten with adhesive tape. If you are working with a small group, give each child a card. If you are working with the whole class, share the cards out one between two or three. All the cards must be given out.

The child (or group) with the card marked * reads the question aloud. The child (or group) with the answer to that question reads out the answer, then reads out the question on the back of that card. This goes on until the first child (or group) has read out the answer on the first card.

Q * A torch uses this as its energy source	**A** things go
Q A battery is one of these	**A** battery
Q Energy can be stored in	**A** a store of energy
Q A device that uses the Sun's energy is said to be	**A** a stretched rubber band
Q A solar-powered calculator uses	**A** solar-powered
Q Solar energy comes from	**A** light energy
Q Electrical energy comes from batteries or from	**A** the Sun
Q Electrical energy can be generated by	**A** the mains
Q Electrical energy is generated in	**A** burning coal
Q Some power stations burn	**A** power stations
Q Humans need energy to keep them	**A** oil or gas
Q We get our energy from	**A** active
Q We need food to	**A** food
Q The wind, Sun, water, coal, oil and gas are all natural	**A** give us energy
Q Not many people have	**A** energy sources
Q In a Jack-in-the-box, energy is stored in	**A** solar heating
Q Energy sources are essential to make	**A** a spring

Energy transfer

Every day, we use or see many things that change **energy** from one type to another. We call them **energy changers**. Here is part of Charlotte's diary for one day. It describes some of the **energy transfers** (energy changes) she saw.

6.20am. Got up. Had shower. The shower changes **electrical energy** to **thermal (heat) energy**. Brushed teeth with electric toothbrush. This **transforms** electrical energy into **movement energy**. It generates **sound energy** too, but that's not a useful transfer.

6.50am. Started car and drove to work. The car uses **diesel** as its **fuel**. Energy **stored** in diesel is transformed into movement energy, plus some electrical energy that is changed into **light energy** by the headlights. Sound is made too, but the only useful sound energy is from the car radio. When the car engine is not running, a **battery supplies** the radio with **electrical energy** to make it work. The battery is a **store** of energy.

7.50am. Arrived at office. Switched on computer to check for e-mail. The computer changes electrical energy into light and sound. Got on with work.

11am. Coffee time. Heather came in. She's bought a wind-up toy for her nephew. It **stores** energy in a spring inside, and this is transformed into movement energy when the spring is **released**. Barbara was feeding the rabbits outside our office. Even the rabbits are energy changers. She gave them stored energy in the form of carrots. The rabbits' bodies change the energy in the **food** into movement energy, sound energy and thermal energy.

Energy transfer

1. What is an energy transfer?____

____

2. Here is a list of types of energy:

electrical	light	movement	sound	stored	thermal (heat)

Choose six energy changers from the text, and write down the main energy change that happens with each one. The first one has been written for you.

shower	electrical	➡	thermal
		➡	
		➡	
		➡	
		➡	
		➡	

3. Now use the same list to write down the energy changes for some devices you might find in the kitchen.

kettle	electrical	➡	
toaster		➡	
clock		➡	
radio		➡	
food mixer		➡	

4. List four things that have energy stored in them.

____

5. Where do humans and other animals get their energy from?

____

Write a diary page about your morning in school. Underline all the energy changers. Then write a list of the energy changers and say what energy transfers happen with each one.

Energy transfer

1. What is an energy transfer?____

____

2. Here is a list of types of energy:

electrical   light   movement   sound   stored   thermal (heat)

Write down what energy change takes place in each of these devices.

shower	electrical	➡	thermal
electric toothbrush	electrical	➡	
car		➡	
computer		➡	

3. Now use the same list to write down the energy changes for some devices you might find in the kitchen.

kettle	electrical	➡	
toaster		➡	
clock		➡	
radio		➡	
food mixer		➡	

4. List four things that have energy stored in them.

________________ ________________ ________________ ________________

5. Where do humans and other animals get their energy from?

____

Write a diary page about your morning in school. Underline all the energy changers. Then write a list of the energy changers and say what energy transfers happen with each one.

More than one type of energy?

These devices change energy into more than one type. Beside each picture, write about the energy transfers. The first one has been done for you.

car

The car changes stored energy in the fuel into movement energy to take you from one place to another. It also transforms the stored energy into light energy for the headlights, sound energy for the radio and electrical energy to charge the battery.

television

computer

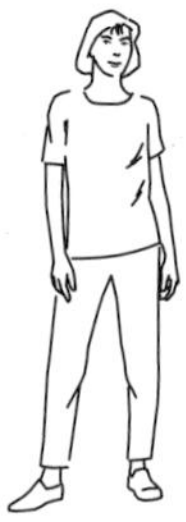

human

fairground ride

Wasted energy

Each of these energy changers produces some types of energy that are useful, and some that are not so useful. The energy that is not useful is wasted.

Next to each picture, write about the wasted energy. The first one has been done for you.

lamp

This lamp changes electrical energy into light energy and thermal energy. The light energy is useful, but the thermal energy is not. If you touch a lit bulb, it may be so hot that you burn yourself.

television

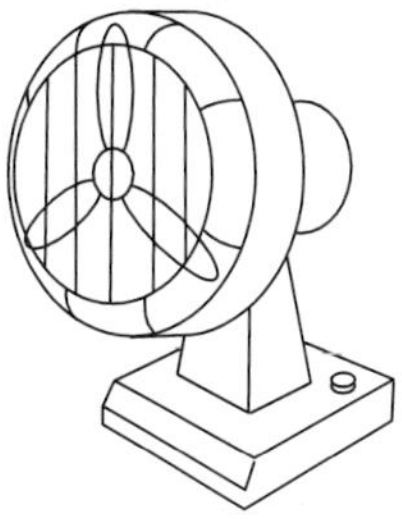

electric fan

car

gas cooker

Stored energy

Energy has been stored in all these things. They are all ready to release energy. Explain how the energy is stored in each one. The first one has been done for you.

Rollercoaster at the top of a slope

Energy is stored in a rollercoaster because of its position. Gravity is pulling it downwards. As it comes down the slope, stored energy is transformed into movement energy.

Wind-up toy

Energy is stored in the toy inside a

____

To make the toy work,

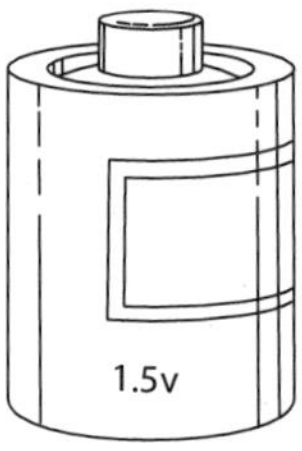

Battery

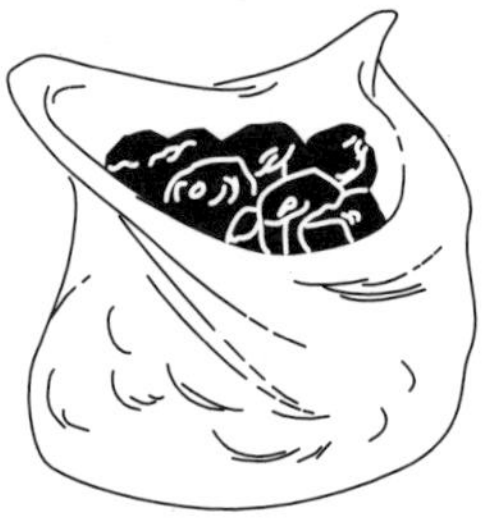

Sack of coal

Water behind a dam

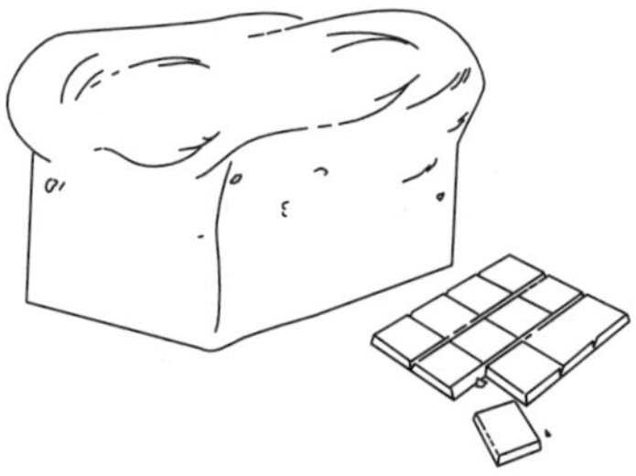

Food

Energy snap

1

To make the game
Photocopy this page onto coloured card and page 96 onto white card. Cut out the cards.

To play the game
1. Lay out all the cards, mixed up and face down, on the table.
2. Each player in the group (2–6 players) picks one white card and one coloured card.
3. If the energy changer on the card either uses the form of energy on the coloured card or produces it as its main function, the player should explain to the group why the cards match (eg 'A light bulb uses electrical energy to make it work'). If the group agrees with the explanation, the player keeps those cards.
4. If the cards don't match (or the match is not explained correctly), they are put back on the table, face down, in the same places.
5. The winner is the player with the most cards at the end. Some cards may be unused.

electrical	thermal (heat)	movement	light	light	stored
movement	electrical	thermal (heat)	stored	light	electrical
movement	stored	movement	electrical	sound	stored
movement	electrical	sound	electrical	stored	electrical
stored	movement	thermal (heat)	sound	stored	movement
sound	thermal (heat)	movement	electrical	light	light

2 Energy snap

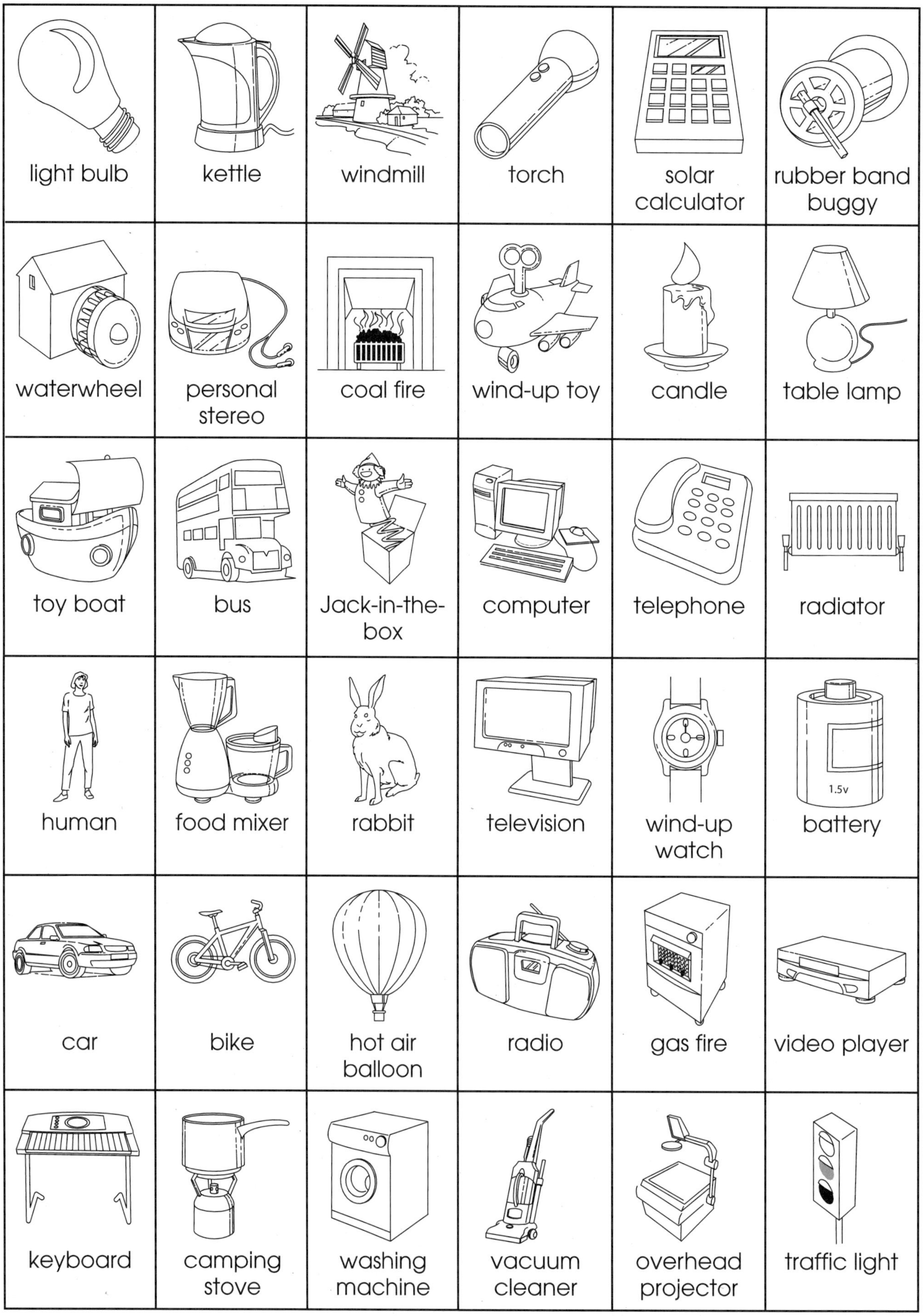